CONSTRUCTION PROJECT ESTIMATING 101

FOR BEGINNERS & NEW GRADUATES

P.D. MASON

INTRODUCTION

Greetings Construction Estimators!

My name is Paul Mason, and I am a construction estimator and a project manager. I've been working in construction for the better part of three decades (27 years, to be exact), and I've been a skilled tradesperson for all those 27 years.

I humbly thank you for your support in discovering this book. This book aims to answer your questions about "how to" or "what is" related to construction estimating and give you a general sense of the industry and the estimating process. As we go through the book, I'll assume you're already working as a construction estimator or considering a career in the estimating field.

If you've read my first book in this series, 'Construction Project Management 101' (Sugardog Publishing 2023), thank you again for your support. If you haven't read that book yet, no worries. The books are ultimately meant to complement each other in the grand scope of working in the construction industry as a project manager or an estimator. Those job titles are often interchangeable as some construction professionals perform both duties while others may work as one or the other. If you feel so inclined, 'Construction Project Management 101' would be a great follow-up book to read that will provide you with an expanded knowledge of the relationship between project management and estimating and the coordination and communication required for both careers.

If this is indeed the first book in the series you are reading, I'll give you some background about myself. I started a skilled trades apprenticeship in the late 1990s. Several years after I started that apprenticeship, I became a Journeyman Plumber, and a few years after that – I became a Master Plumber. I remained in the field running people and large projects for a little over a decade, and during those years, I realized that the daily grind of working in the field and installing plumbing for the next thirty years might not be in my long-term plan.

Throughout my career, I've had the opportunity to travel to different regions of the United States and work on large and small-scale plumbing projects. I've worked in the residential, commercial, and industrial sectors, like refineries and industrial food processing plants.

I started my own plumbing business when the market couldn't sustain my services any longer, and that was a great learning experience. It taught me that starting a service-related business in an economic recession was a great idea, but at face value only. Ultimately, the sustainability of that business in a volatile recession was what I wasn't prepared for. Needless to say, the company was only operating for about three years before I had to find another source of income in my field.

With the recession of the late 2000s, unemployment was at an all-time high. The housing market was in shambles, and that took away most of the income from longtime residential construction companies and their subcontractors.

The plumbing trade in my area was crawling to a halt, and the outlook for future work was not good. I had a decision to make, and in retrospect, it was one of the most challenging life decisions I've ever made – and also the best career decision.

Sometime after the late 2000s, when the media was professing that the "recession was over" and "things would get back to normal," plumbing work and construction as a whole was finally picking up speed. Construction wasn't yet in full force as it was before the housing market crash. Still, it had enough inertia to sustain growth for the conceivable future after the recession.

As work for plumbers was still reasonably light when the construction industry picked up again, I spent only a few days a week working for nearly a year.

While surfing the internet on one of my days off, I saw an employment listing for a Project Management position at a mechanical contractor that I was familiar with by name only. I could tell that a recruiter had written the job posting. Hence, as a skilled tradesperson, I immediately thought I had zero chance of walking into that company as a Master Plumber and walking out with a project management job, as skilled tradespeople typically wouldn't be 'recruited' for jobs.

My reasoning for those initial thoughts came down to my self-doubt that I could ever learn to be a project manager and that I had zero experience as an estimator. For context, I knew the nature of the project management positions at that company. The project managers were also the estimators on the piping and plumbing side of the business.

After sleeping on the decision for a night, I realized I was qualified for the job. As a long-time field foreman, superintendent, and a host of other hats worn in the field, I realized I had been "estimating" for years to friends and family and friends of family friends. As a skilled tradesperson, more specifically a skilled tradesperson that is a plumber, I had given so many 'estimates' to anyone who called me asking "how much to....".

Skilled trades are just what the title implies, which is skilled at performing a job or a task that the not-so-skilled in that task cannot do. I had given more estimates over the previous dozen or so years before I interviewed for that project management position than I had even realized, and that made up my mind whether I would apply for the position.

I was offered a project management position based on my years in the trade, in addition to the fact that I had started my own business a handful of years before I was offered that position. The company's president stated he was willing to take a risk on a guy with the grit to start a business in such a rough economic market, and then he asked me what I had learned from that experience. Although it was a considerable pay cut from what I would have been making if I was gainfully employed in my trade, of which, before that interview, I was only employed half-time or so, thus, I had nothing to lose.

When I started my newly acquired project management and estimator position, that same company president welcomed me on day one, showed me my office, and (anecdotally) said, 'sink or swim'; at least that's what it felt like he said.

There wasn't a company training program, no 'how-to' manual about project management or estimating, and initially, no one to show me the ropes. The only thing Mr. company president told me was that they would schedule me for a business trip to the US East Coast for training on their computer-based estimating program.

That trip was the first time I had ever heard about software-based estimating, and even to this day, I fully understand why the president of that company didn't want to immerse me in project management or estimating immediately. There are no tips or tricks in estimating, and each person has to figure out their processes and methods to arrive at the end result – a solid bottom-line bid number.

I was in that position for the better part of a decade for that company and found much success as a project manager and estimator. Shortly after I arrived at the company, I regularly picked the brain of an 'old-timer' HVAC project manager who took me under his wing and taught me how to refine my methods and processes in project management to be consistent on every job I ran.

The fellow who helped me during those first few years also helped me realize how much of a knack I had for both aspects of my job — project management and estimating. I was very detail-oriented, which is, by nature, an excellent skill for an estimator, and I was "hungry," as they say. I was hungry for work and even more hungry to find success.

I already had the tools I needed within myself to excel as an estimator. When I began my estimating career, I was given the tools (through a software-based estimating program) to do all of the heavy lifting on takeoffs and create accurate material lists - and the rest was up to me.

This book intends to give you every bit of advice, information, and anything else I can think of to help you excel as a construction estimator. It is immaterial that I'm a plumber by trade, as it's just the avenue I took to advance my career to the office side of construction.

The book covers many topics that I was clueless about when I first became an estimator, and in full disclosure, I had to learn the hard way about some of the topics I present in this book. The 'hard way' means I had to sit in the office of the fellow who graciously took me into his company without knowing how I would perform for his company's bottom line. Multiple times, I found myself explaining how I forgot this or that on the bid, and unfortunately, my errors came with monetary losses to the company on a project or two. Fortunately for me, Mr. company president who hired me understood there would inevitably be some bumps in the road, to which he simply would say, "On to the next one".

Construction project estimating is not an exact science, and if it were so easy, 'everyone would be doing it' as they say.

You've made a significant step towards success in your estimating career by understanding that books, articles, how-tos, and maybe even some videos are available that explain what estimating is. How to do it comes from you and comes from within.

I will share much of my construction knowledge regarding estimating with you inside the book. I'll provide some methods that I've used and some processes that will help you become efficient and proficient at estimating.

Most of all, I'll guide you through many elements of construction estimating that took me years to figure out, and had I known certain aspects of estimating right from the start, I can only daydream how my efficiency and workflow would have been better right from the beginning of my career.

That said, welcome aboard, and let's dive into the first chapter!

1

THE FUNDAMENTALS OF COUNSTRUCTION ESTIMATING

Construction estimating is the global foundation of construction projects in that it's the starting point where we carefully predict and calculate the costs involved in building or constructing nearly everything we see around us. Every time you get behind the wheel and drive somewhere, I bet you don't notice how many structures you pass. For every one of those structures, whether it be a house, a doctor's office, a shopping mall, a tattoo parlor, or even a place of worship, someone created an estimate before that structure was built.

This chapter will be similar to a building foundation in that it is intended to be your introduction to Construction Estimating 101. We'll break down the basics for those stepping into the world of figuring out how to create a construction estimate accurately. We will explore the fundamental principles and techniques you need to grasp to understand this often fast-paced side of construction, such as the importance of accuracy in your estimates and building a solid foundation as your go-to starting point when you start a new estimate.

INTRODUCTION TO CONSTRUCTION ESTIMATING

Construction estimating has been a necessary tool and a lucrative career choice for centuries. If you think back to a time when civilization began, let's say the Bronze Age around 3300 BC, someone on that crew of Great Pyramid construction professionals was responsible for the estimation of just how much limestone would be required to build the first pyramid, and likely also had some idea of how long that first pyramid would take to complete.

After that first pyramid was built, a few of the most skilled craftspeople and maybe even the pyramid designer got together and talked about what went well and where they could improve. These conversations still happen frequently in the 21st century, thousands of years after the first pyramid was constructed.

Construction estimating, sometimes called cost estimating, is not an exact science - that's why it's called estimating and not exacting. (See what I did there?). The benefit of having a post-estimate and post-construction debrief of any project tells a story. That story will reveal where the estimate was spot on and can also point out where the estimate was an epic failure.

Whether the estimate was a winner or a loser, the data gathered from estimated project costs versus actual project costs is vital in refining an estimator's methods. Throughout my project management and estimating career, I've had to reexamine my methodology and make refinements and tweaks. With enough data to examine after construction projects are complete, a construction estimator has everything right before them to review when projects of similar types or scopes come across the estimator's desk again. The best part is that the second time you bid on a similar project, you can accurately identify the opportunity to make the same mistakes twice, as you've already combed through some previous post-estimating data and found where you may have fallen short or even overestimated costs.

Through many years of refinements in my estimating processes and attempts to discover the essential core skills I needed to have proficiency in, I developed this list that is an ongoing learning process even though I've been on this side of construction for over a decade and a half.

Here is my list of core principles that a new construction estimator should become familiar with:

- How to Organize an Estimate.
- Markups - Profit and Overhead.
- The Elements of an Estimate.
- Factoring the unknowns (or variables) into your estimate.
- Techniques for Pricing.
- The correct way to estimate labor, equipment, and materials.
- Types of estimates.
- Correct quantity take-off techniques.

Throughout this book, we will discuss the points above and additional skills and techniques to become proficient at construction estimating.

Let's first look at the different construction estimating types (or methods) you'll likely be asked to use as an estimator.

Assembled Estimating. In assembly estimating, instead of bidding on individual components of a project separately, the estimator groups them into assemblies. These assemblies can consist of elements from a single trade or multiple trades. For instance, a simple assembly like a residential light switch includes a single-gang box, a single-pole switch, a cover plate, two wire nuts, and 20 feet of NM-B 12-gauge wire, all installed by an electrician. In a residential electrical estimate, one can use assemblies for switches, outlets, lights, power panels, etc., rather than specifying each component individually.

On the other hand, complex assemblies, like a metal-stud, gypsum-board partition wall, involve various items like bottom track, metal studs, top track, drywall, screws, tape, joint compound, insulation, primer, paint, and more. Multiple trades typically install such assemblies.

Assembly estimating proves beneficial for conceptual and preliminary estimates. A quick estimate for an entire building can be generated using broad assemblies. However, these estimates involve general assumptions and are less precise. They are suitable for projects with limited drawings, for comparing design approaches, and as a cross-check for detailed estimates. While using assembly prices from previous projects, it's crucial to acknowledge that each project is unique, considering factors like weather conditions, building materials, systems, and team members. Skill and judgment are essential to adjust the assembly estimate accurately, accounting for the varying conditions of each project.

Detailed Estimate. The detailed estimate involves figuring out how much of everything is needed to finish a project, including materials, labor, equipment, insurance, bonds, and other costs. It even includes an estimate of the profit. To do this, the contractor needs all the details in the contract documents. Each part of the project is carefully broken down and estimated to understand what's required accurately.

Every task assigned to the contractor comes with its own labor needs, which must be estimated accurately. For items others will install, it's crucial to define and price them accurately. It's essential to make sure both the contractor and subcontractor agree on what each is responsible for – whether it's just installation or supplying and installing. Also, there should be a clear understanding of who provides support items like cranes and scaffolding. The contractor is responsible for dividing the scope of work between themselves and subcontractors, ensuring there's no overlap and that everything is included in someone's scope of work.

When creating a detailed estimate, it's essential to establish estimated quantities and costs for materials, time and labor costs, equipment requirements and their costs, overhead items and their costs, and the desired profit percentage. This considers the investment, time needed to complete the project, and complexity.

Model Estimating. Model estimating employs computer models to generate an estimate based on a set of questions answered by the estimator. This method shares similarities with assembly estimating but involves less direct input from the estimator. For instance, when estimating the cost for a warehouse, the estimator might need to respond to questions such as:

What is the square footage or length of the building?

How many tenant spaces or bays are along the length of the building?

Will wire mesh or rebar be required in the slab?

What is the top wall height above the finished floor?

Starting at grade, what is the depth to the top of the footing?

How wide is the building?

How many egress roof hatches will be required?

If you need overhead doors, how many and what size are you requiring?

What type of bathroom facilities do you want (individual or unisex)?

How many personnel doors are needed?

Do you want skylights, and if so, what size and how many?

How thick is the floor?

Are there bays along the width of the building, and if so, how many?

Based on the responses to these questions, the model generates an initial estimate for the project. Based on the provided answers, the model incorporates logic to select the necessary components for the estimate. For instance, the size and cost of spot footings at the center of the building supporting the roof are determined by the roof area they support, calculated as the width of a bay multiplied by the length of a bay – derived from a few of the questions. However, it makes certain assumptions about the warehouse design, such as using concrete masonry units (CMU) for the exterior wall. It's important to note that the model estimating methods typically exclude site and excavation costs, which must be added to obtain a comprehensive estimate.

Estimating models vary in complexity and can furnish a detailed estimate for the entire project or a preliminary estimate for a specific portion. Similar to square-foot estimates, assembly estimates utilizing broad assemblies, and parametric estimates, caution is necessary to ensure the proposed project aligns with the projects from which the model was developed.

Comparative Project Estimates. Project comparison estimates involve comparing the cost of a proposed project to that of a finished project. When employing this method, the estimator begins with the costs of a similar project and then adjusts for variations in the new project. For instance, when estimating the cost of buildings in an apartment project, the estimator may use a project built with the same plans in the previous year in a nearby city as a reference. However, adjustments are necessary for factors like inflation, labor availability, cost changes, modifications to meet city codes, and other relevant differences.

It's important to note that, in most cases, accurate estimating site work should be done using another method due to the numerous discrepancies in site conditions. Similar to other estimating approaches that don't create a detailed list of materials, caution is essential to ensure that the proposed project closely resembles the completed project used for comparison.

Estimating Using The Square Foot Method. Square-foot estimates involve calculating the cost of a building by multiplying its square footage with the cost per square foot. The resulting price is then adjusted for differences in building heights, perimeter length, and other components. In some cases, measurements other than square footage, such as the number of parking stalls in a garage, may be used to determine the building's size. Unlike detailed estimates, square-foot estimates require less information and can be generated using a schematic set of design drawings, including a single-line floor plan and key elevations. These estimates are useful for checking if a project aligns with the owner's budget. Similar to assembly estimates, caution is needed to ensure that the projects used to determine the cost per square foot are comparable to the proposed project.

Parametric Estimates. Parametric estimates involve utilizing equations that articulate the statistical correlation between various building parameters and the associated building costs. These parameters include gross square footage, number of floors, perimeter length, percentage of common space, and more. The parameters in the equation need to be determinable early in the design phase for the equation to be practical; otherwise, it becomes ineffective. While parametric estimates share similarities with square-foot estimates, the equations employed in parametric estimates are more intricate, incorporating log functions, parameter ratios, and parameter multiplication. Parametric estimating proves valuable for generating conceptual estimates based on assumptions regarding crucial building parameters or estimates grounded in early design concepts. Similar to square-foot estimates and assembly estimates utilizing broad assemblies, caution is necessary to ensure the proposed project aligns with the projects from which the equation was derived.

As you've read, there are multiple methods of construction estimating. Many individual estimators find one particular method they prefer to use, build upon that method, and tailor it to their needs to ensure accuracy for every estimate they perform.

Another baseline skill you will need as an estimator is understanding the construction "divisions." Division is a general term designed to give each discipline in construction (such as carpentry, plumbing, finishes, electrical, earthwork, and more) its own specific set(s) of specifications and regulations. Separating these divisions is a very good way to keep your estimate clean and in order with just a few of these divisions, or even if you are estimating a project that utilizes all divisions, such as an industrial or municipal project.

Understanding the basis of what scope of work each division performs will definitely bolster your understanding of the construction process and, ultimately, the sequencing of construction projects.

Here are the standard construction divisions and their respective division numbers. These divisions and division numbers are defined by the Construction Specifications Institute's (CSI) MasterFormat, which is the most widely used standard for organizing project specifications and other written information for commercial and institutional building projects in the U.S. and Canada.

- Division 01 — General Requirement
- Division 02 — Site Work
- Division 03 — Concrete
- Division 04 — Masonry
- Division 05 — Metals
- Division 06 — Wood and Plastics
- Division 07 — Thermal and Moisture Protection
- Division 08 — Doors and Windows
- Division 09 — Finishes
- Division 10 — Specialties
- Division 11 — Equipment
- Division 12 — Furnishings
- Division 13 — Special Construction
- Division 14 — Conveying Systems
- Division 15 — Mechanical/Plumbing

- Division 16 — Electrical

These sixteen divisions are the most commonly found in project specification books in construction estimating today and, again, are defined by the Construction Specifications Institute's (CSI) MasterFormat. This list is extensive; however, a few modern-day nuances to this list can sometimes confuse a new estimator trying to navigate the divisions.

For instance, this list of Divisions terminates at Division 16 - Electrical. There are indeed divisions that are higher than 16. In fact, a true exhaustive list of construction divisions has been known to reach the upper forties in numerical order. The additional divisions beyond the CSI list above have been subgrouped throughout the years as projects have increased in size and required additional "specialty" contractors to perform certain functions.

Here are some examples of the expanded list:

Division 15 — Mechanical/Plumbing is often split into Division 22 — Plumbing and Division 23 — HVAC. This happened due to some crossover confusion of plumbing piping and HVAC heating and cooling piping being lumped into the same division.

HVAC controls within buildings (think of thermostats or master controls for a boiler system) were usually lumped into Division — 15 Mechanical/Plumbing, but with energy codes and regulations, a building HVAC controls system is now so nuanced that those specifications typically reside under their number of Division — 25 Integrated (or Building) Automation.

The expanded list of divisions is advantageous for a much cleaner project specification book, but it also adds much more for the construction estimator to account for. Understanding the divisions within a construction estimate will be imperative to your success as an estimator.

As we change our topic to accuracy in estimating, please remember that construction estimating is a very refined process of consistency repeatedly — for the sole purpose of your confidence that your methods and processes as an estimator are done the same way every time. Repetition as an estimator is paramount to creating consistency for yourself and for the estimates you produce for others. You want to say confidently that you've accounted for every cost and profit dollar, and consistency is key.

THE IMPORTANCE OF ACCURATE ESTIMATES

Precision in project estimation is crucial for the success of any construction project. Owners and contractors heavily rely on cost estimates to progress a project from preconstruction to completion.

Lacking an initial understanding of a project's costs hampers owners' ability to ascertain its feasibility within the designated budget. Following a preliminary estimate, adjustments to design or scope may become necessary to modify project costs.

Contractors also rely on accurate estimates to formulate competitive and financially rewarding bids. A contractor underestimating a project's cost may need to reduce their profit margin to cover project expenses.

In the craft of construction estimation, professionals, whether employed by a general contractor, specialty contractor, or owner, adhere to a set of fundamental steps. Their primary goal during the construction estimation process is to determine an accurate price for a specific project, often within the context of a competitive or negotiated bidding process.

Typically, construction estimators initiate the process by reviewing bid documents, which encompass construction specifications and contract documents. This initial phase sets the foundation for subsequent steps that involve meticulously considering every identifiable cost, such as materials, labor, insurance, and overhead.

Upon completing the estimation process, the estimator presents a comprehensive construction estimate. This estimate considers all necessary costs and includes a markup designed to cover profit and contingency.

The steps I first learned as a new construction estimator, which have been refined over the years to my liking, were something to the effect of these that are listed below.

Review the bid package or bid invite. The bid invite process involves a bid package that includes essential documents like owner-contractor agreements, bond forms, general conditions, supplementary general conditions, and construction specifications. Professional estimators invest significant time in thoroughly understanding every aspect of the project, as contractors bidding on a project commit to completing the work outlined in the bid package.

Drawings are categorized based on their purpose: site, architectural, structural, mechanical, electrical, and more. General and specialty contractors review these documents, focusing specifically on the documents relevant to their assigned project tasks.

Make a site visit or multiple visits if needed. Conducting a site visit before submitting a bid is usually advisable. Even when not mandatory, estimators find that a comprehensive site visit provides valuable insights into site conditions, surpassing the information available from elevation drawings or photographs of the proposed construction site.

Depending on the project type, specialty contractors might opt for fewer site visits, preferring to depend on documentation supplied by the project's owner and general contractor.

The primary goal of a site visit is to enhance the estimator's understanding of site conditions and their potential impact on project costs.

Understand the quantities needed for the project and create a material takeoff. Estimators create a material or quantity takeoff by thoroughly examining the construction documents and tallying each item essential for the project. The material requirements are usually organized based on their measurement criteria.

Following the completion of a takeoff, estimators obtain a comprehensive list of all materials necessary for project completion. Furthermore, they leverage this takeoff information to ascertain the equipment requirements for each work package.

Estimators can opt for a manual takeoff, employing tools like paper copies of drawings, rulers, highlighters, scale rulers or digital measuring tools, and pencils to count and measure materials based on specifications. In the contemporary landscape, most estimators prefer digital takeoffs facilitated by construction estimating software, significantly expediting the process. Nevertheless, many estimators exercise caution by cross-verifying the digital takeoff's accuracy to ensure their estimate is correct.

Contact vendors and suppliers for material and equipment pricing. With a well-defined materials and equipment list you've created, specialty contractors can begin working with suppliers and vendors to get pricing information.

In cases where contractors don't possess the necessary project equipment, they must contact equipment vendors to establish leasing or rental prices for the project's duration.

Considering the various options of owning, purchasing, leasing, or renting equipment, contractors must assess how the project influences related equipment costs, such as depreciation or maintenance. This information is then integrated into their estimate.

At this point in the estimation process, contractors obtain the initial dollar figures that must be factored in as project costs. Subsequently, estimators will progressively include more direct, indirect, and overhead costs to gain a comprehensive understanding of the actual financial impact of the project from a contractor's perspective.

Identify the labor needed to perform the project. By using the information you've gathered, you can now get a feel for the labor required to perform the project. You will need to identify which skilled trades will be required and the hours required for each trade to complete their parts of the project, and hopefully, you will be able to ascertain the production level of the crew(s) that will be working on the project. Efficiency is a key element of construction projects - and you won't want to scrutinize the labor dollars spent when you're only a portion of the way through a project.

Estimators regularly need to stay abreast of their local labor market and oftentimes may have to calculate a loaded labor rate for each project. If you're unsure of what a loaded rate means, there is a definition in the Glossary at the back of this book.

Gather secondary information such as insurance requirements or bonding requirements. Mitigating risk for both owners and contractors, insurance and bonding are crucial elements in construction projects. However, this risk reduction comes at a price that needs to be factored into project estimates.

General liability insurance is a standard requirement for almost all construction companies. Additional policies may be necessary depending on factors like company size, scope, and role. It is common in construction for the general contractor to carry the lion's share of the insurance requirements for a project. Still, depending on the project and the general contractors' contract with their subcontractors, an estimator may need to factor in insurance such as builders' risk, errors and omissions, or even commercial auto insurance for all project costs.

Understand what the overhead and indirect costs will be. While not explicitly outlined in the bid package, certain costs are essential for project construction. Estimators evaluate the rate and duration of each of these items, considering factors like the required time for a temporary site office.

Apart from these indirect project costs, there are general overhead costs, also called general and administrative (G&A) expenses. These represent the inherent costs of conducting business. Whether or not a contractor has active projects, these expenses must be covered.

Typical direct overhead costs that may be budgeted into a project estimate are things like rent for a project trailer if the project has an extended timeline, administrative payroll if the project needs a project assistant, software subscriptions or direct costs, or utilities might be needed for the project trailer.

Calculate the profit amount and contingency. Contingency figures within the construction industry exhibit substantial variability, depending on factors like the construction type, company size, and project risk. It's common for many construction businesses to incorporate approximately 5-10% of the contract price as a contingency.

Once a contingency determination is calculated, the estimator establishes the sales price encompassing all project costs, including materials, labor, equipment, direct and indirect overhead, and contingency costs. This final figure ensures not only comprehensive coverage of expenses but also should provide a satisfactory profit. Equipped with this calculated amount, estimators can confidently submit competitive bids or initiate negotiations with project owners or general contractors.

Once the sales price is established, you, as the estimator, will generate a construction proposal that provides a detailed breakdown of all components included in the bid price, presented clearly and concisely. Consistency in language is crucial as bid reviewers must ensure that all elements within the scope of work are accounted for in the bid price, aligning with the construction specifications and drawings.

As you progress in your construction estimating career, you'll develop a consistent system of providing thorough and concise estimates.

Remember that consistency is key as we wrap up these baseline fundamentals needed in construction estimating. I think I've already mentioned that once or twice, and I'll likely mention it a few more times throughout the book. An old timer (actually, it was the fellow who took me under his wing that I told you about in the introduction to this book) taught me that every estimate I'll likely ever do is going to have differences from the previous estimate I did and will likely be different from the next estimate I will create — but as long as I'm consistent with how I prepare and deliver estimates, I will never have to second guess myself whether I covered all costs or not.

That was very good advice that still sticks with me today.

The next chapter will examine some vital elements of building a solid estimating foundation.

2

BUILDING A SOLID ESTIMATING FOUNDATION

As a construction estimator, building a solid foundation is a very crucial starting point for a successful career. When you are new to the estimating world, it is hard to imagine what that 'foundation' looks like, and I know this as I've been where you are. As you get your first estimate completed and sent off, then another one, and another one after that, you'll start to have the makings of a process for yourself.

Each of those estimates is like the concrete footings that are the workhorse of support for a building about to be constructed. Each estimate you calculate and deliver is another footing in your foundation, and each estimate you provide should be better than the previous one.

Unfortunately, the processes and methods estimators use are typically under constant refinement; at least for me, they were. You've heard the saying, "You need to walk before you can run," and estimating is no different than the walking part of that saying. Every estimate you create and deliver will be a learning experience for you. As the months and years go by in your estimating career, you'll establish a system, a method, and a pattern for how you like to work and how you like your workflow while estimating.

This chapter will provide you with many foundational workflow ideas that you can expand upon and tailor to what suits your style the best.

ESTABLISHING A CONSISTENT ESTIMATING PROCESS

Ensuring your construction estimates are consistent is vital to a lifelong career as a construction estimator. It not only improves the accuracy of your predictions but also boosts the success of your projects. Nothing can eat up the projected profit margin in construction quite like a wrong estimate. Once you've completed and delivered your estimate, that's the project's price, and there's no turning back. Whether it turns out better or worse, you completed the estimate, and in some regards, you own the project's outcome.

Accurate estimates are the backbone of successful construction projects, so your approach to each estimate must be calculated and purposeful. The key to tackling these challenges is a structured, consistent process.

With a solid individualized system in place, you're better equipped to handle whatever projects come your way.

There are many schools of thought about why consistency in construction estimating is essential. There are benefits to consistency that some estimators won't even realize until they've been performing their job for multiple years.

Here are a few examples of the benefits that come with regular consistency in your estimates:

> **Speed.** Construction estimating is naturally slow and involves a deep dive into costs, materials, labor prices, and more. Unfortunately, none of this happens quickly, and in construction, time is money. The goal of consistent construction estimating is to trim down this time-consuming process to the bare minimum.

Accuracy. Accuracy is paramount. Simple mistakes can throw off an estimate, leading to trouble down the line in the project. A more straightforward process prevents errors from creeping in and ensures they're caught and corrected if they slip through.

Efficiency. Efficiency gets a boost when there's greater consistency in construction estimating. It simplifies spotting trends and comparing data from one project to the next. This means less time figuring out the basics for each estimate and more time focusing on the unique aspects of each project.

Spotting and fixing a regularly under or overestimating pattern becomes much more straightforward with consistent construction estimating. By maintaining the same format, style, or level of detail in your estimates, you create a framework that highlights issues, allowing you to address them proactively.

The benefits of consistent construction estimating go beyond just saving time. It leads to more accurate estimates and facilitates a proactive learning process from project to project. This approach empowers you to make informed choices and improve your estimating accuracy.

Establishing a clear and understandable process for yourself is an excellent strategy for achieving consistency in construction estimates. The whole estimating goal is to eliminate conflicting information and refine your estimating techniques across different projects.

Ensuring a successful construction project hinges on delivering a high-quality outcome that surpasses client expectations. The foundational step in achieving this excellence lies in the estimation process, particularly in generating an accurate takeoff to identify the right quantities. These quantities are pivotal in determining cost and schedule, forming the basis of your overall estimate.

In the fast-paced construction industry, ongoing innovation provides various resources to enhance the accuracy and usefulness of the estimation process. An accurate estimate benefits the current project and safeguards your bottom line. Costly mistakes in estimation can have far-reaching consequences, potentially taking all of the built-in profit out of a project. Therefore, staying abreast of industry advancements and leveraging precise estimation techniques and methods is crucial for success in construction endeavors.

CREATING AN EFFECTIVE WORKFLOW

Suppose you've spent time as an estimator in the construction industry. In that case, you've already likely realized that being awarded the latest and greatest high-profile project is a great accomplishment for you as an estimator. Additionally, as you're probably working for a general or specialty contractor, being awarded projects you've completed the estimate for shines a certain amount of successful light on you as the estimator who won the contract.

If you're just starting as an estimator in the industry and have landed your first estimating job, congratulations on your new position, and rest assured that you'll become comfortable in your skin as an estimator in no time.

I remember the first few 'solo' estimates I did and how I would stare at my takeoffs for hours, simply wishing (more like daydreaming) that the lightbulb would turn on above my head and I'd magically discover every penny of cost I hadn't accounted for. That's not real life, unfortunately. In those first few months, I realized that I needed to get a grip on my processes and figure out what was working and what wasn't. It was my workflow that was the problem. Short of using the word "scatterbrained," I didn't have a logical process. I dove in right away and head first for my first few takeoffs without spending the necessary time to familiarize myself with every document available for those first projects. In essence, my workflow was horrible. I wasn't logically moving along in the process. I was jumping around from task to task to get an estimate completed.

Having your own personalized "workflow" will tremendously help you refine the methods and processes used to complete your estimates.

If you're unfamiliar with workflow, here's a layman's definition.

> **Workflow**. Workflow refers to the steps, tasks, or processes designed and followed to achieve a specific outcome or goal within a particular business, project, or system. Workflows are often organized sequences of activities that define how work is structured, executed, and managed. They can involve the coordination of tasks, the flow of information, and the allocation of resources to ensure a streamlined and efficient progression from the initiation of a task to its completion. Workflows are commonly used in various fields, including business and construction, project management, software development, and manufacturing. Workflow is beneficial to optimize processes, enhance productivity, and maintain consistency in the execution of tasks.

Creating construction estimates is a labor-intensive aspect of bidding, involving substantial time analyzing project features. Complicating matters, material and equipment prices regularly fluctuate with market changes, sometimes leading to inaccuracies when the final bid is presented.

Swift completion of estimates is advantageous, ensuring up-to-date and precise pricing. Faster estimates mean more bids are sent, and more bids submitted should lead to potentially winning more projects. Rapid proposals also position a team as highly competent against competitors.

An estimator with a refined workflow process can quickly free up 10-15 hours a week to focus on tasks such as gathering data from past estimates that might allow you an advantage for upcoming project bids. Additionally, this time can be redirected towards higher-value tasks like value engineering and identifying optimal trade partners.

There are ways you can streamline your estimating methods and processes, and realistically, most of the ways a construction estimator streamlines is through trial and error. However, it's important to note that you may discover a method that might work for an industrial processing plant where you are the lead estimator. However, will that method be equally efficient if you estimate a new big box store or a tenant build-out? You'll most likely have to revise your methodology on the industrial processing plant to a smaller-scale project.

There are many ways to refine your estimating process with strategic measures. These include leveraging cutting-edge technology, tapping into historical data, and having a systematic workflow that helps you to stay on task. By incorporating these strategies, you can simplify your workflow and improve the accuracy of your estimates.

Here are some tips I learned early on in my estimating career that proved to be beneficial to improve my workflow.

> **Improve estimating efficiency by adopting a common framework.** Standardized templates and processes facilitate seamless transfer of information between projects, reducing time spent on tedious tasks. This enhances data input efficiency and enables quicker, more accurate calculations.
>
> Additionally, standardized processes contribute to practical team training by establishing a consistent work method. This joint approach simplifies the estimating process, ensuring everyone follows cohesive procedures. Not only does this streamline operations, but it also enhances the overall reliability of estimates.
>
> **Feedback is crucial as an estimator.** Regularly assess your input to enhance the quality, accuracy, and reliability of your estimate. Implement consistent methods and tools for collecting and analyzing data. This process lets you regularly review and update estimating processes, incorporating lessons from completed projects.

Ensure consistently updating critical areas, such as material databases, to align pricing with industry rates. Additionally, regularly review and adjust labor rates based on competitive circumstances, such as skilled labor availability and shortages. This continual refinement ensures that your estimating methods remain relevant and reflect the changing dynamics impacting the construction industry.

Simplify the process. Establishing clear roles and responsibilities for each team member involved in the construction estimating process is crucial for simplification. This approach prevents confusion, minimizes duplication of items, and eliminates knowledge gaps.

To enhance networking, create an environment where information seamlessly flows between project managers, engineers, and other stakeholders. Implement singular correspondence methods to keep people informed and centralize crucial conversations, ensuring everyone can access important information. This creates a streamlined and efficient workflow within the construction estimating team.

Enhance estimating practices by applying past lessons. Collect and analyze project data consistently to draw insights for future improvements. By studying relevant metrics, identify patterns and trends, allowing adjustments for better performance and outcomes. This process deepens understanding of cost drivers, risks, and everyday challenges.

For a more focused approach, review cost data from completed projects. Identify consistent over or underestimations to make informed adjustments for future project expenses. This proactive analysis contributes to the ongoing refinement of estimating processes.

Utilize available technology. Streamline the estimating process by investing in construction estimating software. User input-driven software digitally measures lengths or distances, instantly calculates quantities, assigns pricing, and automates costs.

Estimating software generates detailed reports, conducts data analysis, and provides comprehensive cost breakdowns to enhance accuracy. This ensures a clear overview for estimators, reducing errors and inaccuracies. Additionally, the software adapts to project changes, allowing easy updates to quantities and expenses as the project evolves.

For optimal accuracy, choose trade-specific estimating software tailored to your trade. This software maintains an updated database on material demands, labor pricing, and building requirements for your specialty, ensuring precision in your estimates.

UTILIZING TECHNOLOGY FOR EFFICIENT ESTIMATING

The last tip I presented to you above was by design. Construction estimating standalone software and online programs have streamlined the estimating methods, processes, and workflows for anyone estimating within the construction industry.

These programs are very technologically advanced and have "lightened the load," as the saying goes for estimators. Although these programs often have an upfront cost, and some may even have subscription-based ongoing expenses, the investment is well worth the reward.

When I first became a construction estimator, I remember that the first task I gave myself was to create a "takeoff sheet" laid out to my liking, and I used a word processing program to create this sheet. It was nothing more than a tally sheet with columns with headings and rows where I could write the material counts, labor hours, and any specialty items I needed to account for.

The columns were laid out with headings like "quantity" or "labor hours," and I think I even had "unit cost" and "total cost."

Software-based estimating programs were not prevalent when I started as an estimator. Now, there are estimating programs that do everything I was tallying and more with just a few computer mouse clicks.

I am fully invested in computer-based estimating, and because of that, I feel like I'm stepping back into the prehistoric era when I occasionally have to dust off my self-made tally sheets and create an estimate "like they did in the olden days."

These are likely a few of the most prolific time-saving reasons for creating a computer-based estimating workflow.

Repetition. When you're performing takeoffs for structures with repeated spaces such as classrooms, apartments, hotels, dormitories, hospitals, exam rooms in clinics, or anything similar — you're likely familiar with the tedious process of conducting takeoffs for each room separately. Construction takeoff software allows you to streamline this task by performing the takeoffs once and then applying the quantity results to all rooms with identical layouts.

Changes to Construction Documents. It will inevitably happen while you are an estimator. Imagine you've just finished "stripping a plan" (a common term while using software-based takeoff programs), and a day or two later, you receive the latest revisions to the drawings. You discover a plethora of changes released on the revised set of blueprints. Before software-based estimating programs were mainstream, an estimator would spend hours deciphering the changes, noting which changes were relative to your scope of work, and then re-tallying the changes by hand and adjusting the estimate accordingly. This leaves the door open to underestimating something, which could result in profit loss, or, if you overestimated the changes — that likely would mean your estimate and resulting project bid would be too high, and you wouldn't get the project.

In a software-based estimating program, it's as simple as uploading the revised drawings into the program and "overlaying" the revised drawing on top of the same drawing to spot the differences. Many software-based estimating programs take this process a step further. They will visually indicate the changes from the former drawing to the revised drawing by using contrasting color indicators on each of the drawings—no more hunting and searching to spot the differences on blueprints if the revisions aren't indicated. Technology is an excellent tool for an estimator, and identifying revisions on a blueprint using software that can instantly spot the differences is undoubtedly a timesaver.

Self-Performing the Takeoff. A construction estimator's counting and blueprint reading skills must be top-notch; that's very apparent. Whether you're estimating plumbing, electrical, HVAC, doors, windows, or anything else within a structure, a software-based estimating program can nearly automate those counting tasks. Many programs have a feature where you click on as many points of the blueprint as needed, and then you can give those collective points or dots on the drawing a value. That value might be windows of a specific size, valves that might be needed in a plumbing system, or even electrical receptacles. The point is you have to identify the points on the map (the map is the blueprint on your screen), and then you indicate to the program what those points on the map are — and in just a few clicks that may have taken 5 to 10 seconds to complete, you've now taken off a bundled amount of the same item.

Performing your takeoff electronically leaves little room for error. Most programs count the footage needed for whatever you're taking off, and depending on the program, they can also give you a baseline price for whatever materials are required for that takeoff. As the estimator, this feature also provides an accurate material list you can send to vendors for accurate material pricing.

It is safe to say that computer-based estimating programs have reshaped the way estimators perform their duties, and these programs continue to evolve into efficient, time-saving methods for estimators.

As we close out this chapter, always remember that just as computer-based estimating programs have evolved into fantastic tools for us to use, we also need to evolve with the technology available to us.

Artificial Intelligence in construction estimating is on the horizon, just as it's already being used in many other industries. The future of AI in construction estimating might mean that a blueprint needs to be uploaded into a program, and after a few clicks of the mouse to set your specifications for the project, a minute or two might pass, and the program spits out a perfect takeoff by just using artificial intelligence to perform the takeoff.

In the next chapter, we will discuss some aspects of construction estimating that are key to becoming a successful estimator and will further advance your processes and methods.

3

KEY ELEMENTS OF CONSTRUCTION ESTIMATING

As we start breaking down elements of the estimating process, our focus will go beyond the technical aspects of estimating project costs. We've already established a broader spectrum of successful construction project management by emphasizing the significance of a well-defined workflow. Additionally, we've explored how a systematic and efficient workflow contributes to accurate cost estimation and project success.

Understanding the marketplace you are estimating in is identified as another pivotal element. In this chapter, we will learn about the importance of market research and recognizing the dynamics that influence construction projects. By understanding the interconnectedness of marketplace understanding and estimating, you will gain the knowledge to set the stage for a comprehensive fundamental understanding beyond the takeoff counts and dollars needed for an estimate.

Additionally, this chapter emphasizes the importance of doing your diligence in the context of construction estimating. It underscores the need to thoroughly understand project scopes and the techniques used to understand project specifications.

This diligence involves scrutinizing project details, techniques, and codes and staying informed about construction industry pricing trends. By emphasizing the importance of diligence, as an estimator, you will approach construction estimating with a meticulous and thoughtful mindset, ensuring that every critical aspect is accounted for in the estimation process.

We will also look at some time management methods that are beneficial to increasing your workflow without increasing your workload. As an estimator, you'll never want to feel a deadline looming, which will affect your productivity and could lead to errors or even omissions in the estimate.

UNDERSTANDING THE PROJECT SCOPE AND REQUIREMENTS

Defining the parameters of a construction project stands out as a crucial and demanding responsibility for a construction estimator. The scope outlines the project's deliverables and the methodology for execution and identifies the resources and time constraints that may impact the project. An explicit and practical scope is instrumental in efficiently estimating, executing, and managing the project, preventing scope creep, conflicts, and unnecessary costs.

Throughout my decade and a half of being an estimator and a project manager, I wouldn't consider myself a scope expert, nor would I agree that I enjoy reading a 300-page specification for a large project I'm about to start an estimate for. If you're new to construction estimating and you've never read through a project specification book (commonly called a 'spec book') cover to cover — you're in for a treat. The treat might not be as sweet as you'd like, but it's a treat nonetheless.

It took me a good number of months when I started as an estimator to understand the language a spec book is written in. Architects and engineering firms seem to have a language that only those who know the secret handshake are privileged to understand. However, after your first few project specification read-throughs, you'll get the hang of it.

When I'm prepping for an estimate, the first thing I do is download the project plans and then download the project specifications. This has been part of my workflow from likely the day I started as an estimator, and I still do it today. Once I have the project plans uploaded into my estimating software, I'll start reading the applicable sections to my scope of work. I take notes as I read through the spec sections specifically so I don't have to go back in a moment of panic if the bid day or bid time is looming and I need to modify the takeoff.

Good workflow equals a lightened workload. It's just smart estimating practice.

For someone new to the industry and new to estimating, here are a few of the initial vital targets I would suggest you work towards. These targets will provide you with a great process and some foundational methods from the start. These are not meant to be taken in any order, as you'll need to figure out your personalized workflow.

> **Know the critical project objectives.** This involves recognizing the project objectives and understanding the sought-after outcomes or advantages. These objectives must harmonize with the requirements and anticipations of project stakeholders, including the owner, client, end-users, and regulators. Employ diverse tools and methodologies—such as interviews, surveys, workshops, brainstorming, and SWOT analysis—to gather and evaluate stakeholder requirements. Project objectives must adhere to the SMART criteria, ensuring they are specific, measurable, achievable, relevant, and time-bound.

> **Identify the project deliverables.** This step involves outlining the project deliverables, encompassing the tangible products or services the project aims to generate. These deliverables must align with the project objectives and fulfill stakeholder requirements. Employing a

work breakdown structure (WBS) can assist in breaking down the project deliverables into more manageable components, including phases, tasks, subtasks, and milestones. The WBS should encompass all essential and adequate work required to accomplish the project deliverables, excluding extraneous elements.

Start formulating the project scope letter. Your prepared project scope statement is a formal document that outlines the project scope. This statement should encompass critical elements such as the project objectives, deliverables, acceptance criteria, assumptions, exclusions, and constraints. The project scope statement must exhibit clarity, conciseness, and consistency, earning approval from pivotal project stakeholders. As a foundational reference, the project scope statement is crucial in planning, executing, and controlling the project scope.

Crafting the project scope management plan. Preparing the project scope management plan means creating a supplementary component of the project management plan that outlines how the project scope will be handled throughout its lifecycle. This plan should encompass critical processes such as scope planning, definition, validation, and control. Additionally, it should detail roles and responsibilities, tools and techniques, communication methods, and change management procedures pertinent to managing the project scope. The project scope management plan is a comprehensive guide for effective scope management throughout the project's lifecycle.

Validate your project scope. Validating the project scope is a process that involves securing formal approval of the finished project deliverables from the project stakeholders. This validation process guarantees that the project deliverables align with the acceptance criteria, meet stakeholder requirements, and adhere to established quality standards and regulatory requirements. Inspections, tests, audits, reviews, and feedback from project stakeholders are employed to facilitate validation. Additionally, the validation process documents any changes, issues, or lessons learned that emerge during the project execution.

Take control of the project scope. This last point is essential as the focus shifts to controlling the project scope—an ongoing process of overseeing and handling any alterations to the project scope that transpire during the project lifecycle. This control process guarantees that changes to the project scope are justified, officially approved, and thoroughly documented, with no detrimental impact on project objectives, deliverables, or performance. Additionally, the control process involves updating the project scope statement, the work breakdown structure (WBS), and the project management plan as needed. Various tools and techniques, including change requests, change logs, variance analysis, and performance reports, are employed in the control process.

These six key targets are the basis of any project scope of work, whether commercial, industrial, or residential. An excellent understanding of what a project scope says and implies paves the way for a successful project every time. I'll expand on a few of these further for you to better understand the key targets.

Let's start with project deliverables. The "Identify the project deliverables" section offers a comprehensive breakdown of all project milestones and deliverables, outlining the tasks to be accomplished at each project lifecycle stage. It is crucial to provide contractors and subcontractors with a precise understanding of their responsibilities to ensure that each deliverable aligns with the standards outlined in the project plan. This section is a detailed guide to facilitating effective communication and collaboration among project stakeholders to achieve the desired outcomes.

The "Know the key project objectives" section above could also be shortened to "Scope Details." A scope details section delves deeper into the project, offering intricate information about the precise tasks and technical specifications linked to each deliverable. This section thoroughly describes the individual steps, methods, and techniques contractors will employ to accomplish each aspect of the project. While the "Project Deliverables" section outlines the "what" of the project, the "Scope Details" answers the "how," providing a granular understanding of the methodologies and approaches that will be applied. This section enhances clarity and serves as a guide for executing tasks precisely.

There are also a few clarifications about a few of the terms listed in the key targets that could realistically be included in multiple of the six key targets we discussed.

Take the project timeline and schedule, for example. The timeline and schedule component comprises deadlines and a list of tasks and subtasks associated with each deliverable. While not requiring an exhaustive level of detail, the objective is to furnish contractors with sufficient information to facilitate strategic planning around project milestones. This component serves as a roadmap, enabling contractors to align their efforts with the established timeline, ensuring a coordinated and timely completion of tasks and subtasks for each deliverable.

Another partially classifiable element mentioned in the above vital targets is project management. An additional important component to be incorporated in your Statement of Work (SOW) is the "Project Management" section. This segment is dedicated to delineating the administrative processes integral to the project. It covers aspects such as the protocol for handling change orders, the payment release schedule for contractors, and a comprehensive record of contract terms and legal requirements. A project management section or statement serves as an umbrella framework, establishing the guidelines and procedures governing project-related administrative activities and ensuring clarity and adherence to contractual obligations.

As we round out this subtopic, I'll tell you that having a well-defined and clear scope of work is essential when submitting a construction bid or estimate. Here are a few more tips about how a clear scope of work protects the estimator (and, ultimately, the company you work for).

Avoid scope of work mistakes. Clarity in the Scope of Work is paramount as it reduces the likelihood of contractors having to rectify completed work. Sometimes rectification (or re-work) is essential, but it usually comes with associated costs in terms of time and money. Determining responsibility for these costs can introduce unnecessary stress into a working relationship. Therefore, establishing clear expectations upfront minimizes the need for corrections, fosters smoother collaboration, and avoids potential tensions over financial and time implications.

The Right People For The Job. Ensuring the project stays on track hinges on having the appropriate workforce on-site at the right time. This task becomes intricate in the absence of a clear scope of work. Subcontractors and partners often schedule their commitments months in advance, making it challenging to secure the necessary talent for the project without meticulous advanced planning. A well-defined scope of work becomes a strategic tool, allowing for effective coordination and timely arrangements to secure the required expertise when needed.

Timely Arrival of Materials and Equipment. In an often volatile supply chain climate, proactive planning emerges as a crucial strategy for contractors to complete projects on time successfully. A clear scope of work facilitates the meticulous planning and scheduling of deliveries, ensuring that essential components arrive on-site when needed. Without such clarity, items with long lead times may pose a risk, potentially causing delays in critical project tasks. Therefore, a well-defined scope of work enhances efficiency and helps navigate challenges in the supply chain, contributing to the overall timely completion of the project.

Just as the estimate and project scope letter are nearly the most essential elements of a winning bid, the key targets are just as important as they ensure your methodology in your estimate remains consistent and on task.

CONSTRUCTION COST ESTIMATES EXPLAINED

The initial concept regarding a construction cost estimate is that an estimate is an approximation. As projects unfold, unforeseeable challenges may arise, potentially increasing costs. Alternately, opportunities to save on expenses or materials may also be identified. Consequently, it is common for a project to undergo several estimates throughout its lifecycle.

As outlined by the American Society of Professional Estimators (ASPE), there are five progressive levels of construction estimates. Each level accurately surpasses the preceding one and reveals a more detailed perspective.

Below are the explanations for the five estimate levels defined by the ASPE.

Level 1 - Order of Magnitude Estimate. This is an initial, high-level calculation often done informally, providing a directional indication of costs. It serves the purpose of assessing project feasibility but lacks detailed accuracy.

Level 2 - Schematic Design Estimate. Based on the schematic design, this estimate is valuable for construction companies to decide whether further project exploration is worthwhile.

Level 3 - Design Development Estimate. A rough estimate is formulated from the initial design, providing a more detailed projection of costs as the design progresses.

Level 4 - Construction Document Estimate. Based on the proposed blueprints and building specifications, this estimate offers a more precise calculation as the project's details become more defined.

Level 5 - Bid Estimate. The final estimate is presented by a contractor, incorporating all available blueprints, plans, and material costs. This is the definitive estimate provided to the customer, serving as the basis for the project's financial aspects.

As stated above, the American Society of Professional Estimators determines these five estimate levels and shouldn't be considered gospel in the estimating world. I rarely see estimates referred to as a certain level, but it occasionally happens. You will most likely see a level designation for an estimate if you estimate a municipal or Government project. I can confidently tell you that memorizing these levels and their details is not imperative to success as a construction estimator.

Another similar perspective to the ASPE levels listed above is an estimate naming convention that involves classifying estimates based on their intended use. In this context, estimates can be categorized into three distinct types, each serving a specific purpose.

Design Estimates. They are geared towards creating a quote for a customer or analyzing a project for internal purposes during the design phase. These estimates help assess the project's feasibility and form a preliminary understanding of costs.

Bid Estimates. Specifically crafted for the bidding process, these estimates provide a comprehensive calculation based on all available project details, blueprints, and material costs. Bid estimates serve as the foundation for contractor proposals presented to potential clients.

Control Estimates. Employed for internal project management purposes, control estimates are utilized during the execution phase to monitor and manage costs effectively. These estimates assist in maintaining financial control and tracking project expenses against the budget.

Just as there are many construction estimates, there are also multiple pricing designations, each incorporating specific elements and features.

The most recognized of all the methods of estimating, the three most typical approaches are:

Unit Pricing. Unit pricing is a prevalent method for pricing various products and services. Take, for instance, the scenario of a carpet installation company that charges a base rate per square foot – this represents the unit price. The key lies in factoring in both direct and indirect costs.

Unit cost estimating is particularly effective for determining direct costs. Direct labor costs per hour and material costs per ton or pallet are known quantities. A substantial portion of the estimate can be swiftly completed by pricing out these unit costs. The subsequent step involves accounting for indirect costs.

Consider hiring a subcontractor for electrical work, arranging a follow-up inspection, or covering supervision costs for an in-house crew. Additional overhead, such as safety fencing on construction sites, falls under indirect costs, even though it doesn't align with unit pricing.

Estimating indirect costs can be challenging, making it advisable to use software for accurate tracking. Relying on traditional methods like paper and pencil increases the risk of errors.

Square Footage Pricing. When speed is crucial, square footage pricing becomes valuable for providing a rapid estimate rather than an exact one. For instance, a quick preliminary estimate serves its purpose when facing bid deadlines.

While offering a ballpark figure as an official bid might seem daring, negotiations and potential adjustments during the project's course are expected. Project costs often change, making the initial bid a starting point rather than a final figure.

Square footage pricing involves assessing the project's square footage and basic scope of work to generate a rough estimate efficiently. The advantage of this approach is the ability to submit a higher number of quotes compared to more precise estimates. For instance, creating a square footage estimate in an hour allows for the submission of multiple bids, whereas a more detailed estimate taking 10 hours limits the number of bids that can be submitted. This method aligns with the understanding that the bid price is not the final project cost, and adjustments are expected as the project progresses.

The Rule of Two. The Rule of Two introduces a slightly distinct approach to creating a preliminary estimate, particularly effective for direct costs. Unlike other methods, it acknowledges the inherent difficulty in predicting and varying the nature of indirect costs across different projects.

The Rule of Two operates on the premise that approximately half of any construction project's costs are attributed to labor. For seasoned contractors with experience, estimating the number of person-hours required for a job is a feasible task. For example, calculating labor costs becomes straightforward if a job can be completed in five days with a three-person crew. Double that amount, add 10%, and derive a rough estimate.

While the Rule of Two provides a valuable baseline, it has limitations. Diverse job sites and unique project challenges mean that adjustments to the estimate are inevitable. This adaptability is a regular aspect of the construction process, and experienced contractors anticipate and navigate these adjustments as a routine part of project management.

A reliable construction cost estimate eliminates guesswork from budgeting and enhances the likelihood of attracting new business. Knowing and understanding the appropriate method and using an efficient template streamlines the estimation process, ensuring that you can confidently project the cost of your next project. By combining the right approach with effective tools, you can establish accurate budgets and present accurate estimates that contribute to the success and growth of your estimating career.

As we've read in this topic, achieving an accurate cost estimate for your construction project involves managing multiple precise components that need careful cross-referencing to ensure accuracy. Take the time to methodically think through each stage of the estimate, considering both the apparent and less obvious factors. Prevent unwelcome surprises in your estimate by learning from common mistakes, maintaining organizational discipline, and optimizing efficiency within your workflow. By doing so, you're just one accurate estimate away from securing a successful bid and moving forward with your project!

TIME MANAGEMENT FOR ESTIMATORS

I'm sure you've heard this saying — *Time is money*. Nowhere does this statement ring more true than in construction. Imagine a crew of four carpenters building a wood frame stud wall. The lead carpenter told his boss the previous afternoon that by a specific time on the next work day, the carpenters would be out of wood framing members, and the boss should order more.

The boss immediately jumps on the phone, orders the lumber, and is given a delivery window of 10:30 am to 11 am the next day. At 11:30 am on the delivery day, the boss was walking the construction site and saw the four carpenters sitting on buckets, laughing and joking with each other. As the boss walks by, he scowls at the lead carpenter as productivity and forward progress have all but come to a halt.

The lead carpenter explained the lumber delivery was late and they were out of lumber.

Due to a vendor delivery being late, four skilled carpenters have nothing to do, so they decide to wait for the delivery.

Whether this was an avoidable scenario is immaterial. What is essential to understand is the late delivery just ate up a percentage of the projected project profit, and the productivity of the four carpenters was a costly, unforeseen circumstance that no estimator should ever have to account for. Unfortunately, scenarios like the carpenters and the delivery happen frequently.

Inefficiencies or a loss of productivity in construction is a regular scenario, and an estimator is not expected to "predict" when, how, why, or on which project these productivity losses will occur.

This is just one scenario where an estimator provided the labor hours needed to install the wall but couldn't predict that there would be downtime during the workday due to a no-show delivery.

There are many scenarios like this that happen regularly in construction.

Here are just a few to consider:

- Omitting Project Assistant or Project Management time from the estimate.
- Permit inspections or tests that a municipality requires, or need to be given twice due to an initial inspection failure.
- Client or General Contractor delays within the information funnel.
- Weather delays.
- Holidays, training new employees, or absences from work due to personal issues.
- Socializing on the job site during working hours instead of during break times or lunch breaks.

This list was just a glimpse into the delays I've seen in my estimating career, and each time I encounter an unforeseen delay or a reduction in productivity, I attempt to factor those delays into future estimates of the same type of project.

Two additional points I will give you regarding time management as an estimator are that they are more easily controlled and tailored for you as an estimator.

The first is to be in control of your own time. If you're in the middle of a significant takeoff and feeling the pinch of the looming deadline for a bid, it's quite acceptable to barricade yourself in your office or work area and continue your progress. Even as an estimator assumedly working in an office-type setting, a slight interruption in your productivity can take many minutes or hours to get back on track.

Second, I would remind you that prioritization of your tasks is imperative. Whether reading a spec book to familiarize yourself with a project or making a dozen phone calls to secure vendor pricing, prioritize your tasks to keep the workflow moving forward.

When I was a new estimator and found myself in a position where I would forget what tasks to prioritize and check off the list, I started using lists as my prioritization method. Even to this day, I make lists. Every day before heading home from work, I have a list ready for the next day's tasks, and as new tasks pop up, I prioritize them and list them for the next work day.

We've covered a plethora of information in this chapter, and as you continue to read this book — remember you need to walk before you can run. I've been able to refine every method and process I present to you in this book for years. If you're new to estimating and the information in this book seems daunting, take a break. Set the book down for an hour or two and then come back to it.

In the next chapter, we will look at different estimating scenarios and how to adapt to those scenarios.

4

ADAPTING TO DIFFERENT ESTIMATING SCENARIOS

WITHOUT A DOUBT, someone, somewhere, is paying for the project in any construction bidding or estimating scenario. That someone might be an individual, a company representative, a building ownership group, or even a purchasing official for a municipality.

Whoever is paying the bill for the new building you are creating an estimate for, one thing is sure — the owner's primary concern is achieving the lowest overall project cost, taking into account factors such as the nature, size, and location of the project, as well as the management organization.

While construction cost is a significant component, other factors should not be overlooked. For instance, land acquisition costs substantially affect building construction expenses in high-density urban areas. Additionally, construction financing costs, particularly in large projects like nuclear power plants, can be comparable to the construction cost.

From the owner's perspective, estimating each proposed facility's operation and maintenance costs is crucial for analyzing life cycle costs. The neglect in the past to fully consider the implications of operation and maintenance costs during the design stage is evident in the substantial expenditures required for facility maintenance, especially for publicly owned infrastructure.

Construction budgets typically include allowances for contingencies or unexpected costs during construction. Based on historical experience and the expected difficulty of the project, this contingency amount may be distributed across cost items or consolidated into a single category of construction contingency. Design development changes, schedule adjustments, general administration changes, wage rates, differing site conditions, and third-party requirements imposed during construction are all considered in estimating contingency amounts. Unspent contingency funds can be released to the owner or allocated for additional project elements near the end of construction.

This chapter primarily focuses on differences in how you would estimate different structures based on industry, location, available infrastructure, whether the construction is ground up or renovation, and more.

RESIDENTIAL CONSTRUCTION ESTIMATING.

Just about anywhere you go in the United States, Canada, and even some parts of Mexico, new residential construction has not seemed to stall in the past decade. Residential construction has seemingly risen from the ashes of the US housing market crash of the late 2000s, and the market keeps building more domiciles.

But what does it take to create an estimate for a residential house? Aren't they all cookie-cutter and nearly the same? My short answer is yes, but the answer is no.

In 2008, just before the United States housing market collapsed, the average square foot price to build a brand new house was just over $88.00 per square foot. Statistica.com states that US residential construction encompasses dwelling units classified as single-family units, manufactured housing (mobile homes and modular homes defined as controlled environment built), duplexes, quadplexes, and apartments or condominiums.

The 2008 square foot cost of building a house (also provided by Statistica) is somewhat subjective, given the many classifiable residential dwellings I just listed above.

Regardless of 2008's subjective cost per square foot figure, at today's mid-2020s pricing, that same home used to calculate the 2008 square foot price would be nearly $180.00 per square foot. That's almost a 52% increase in the cost per square foot to build in the residential sector in the mid-2020s.

An example of those factors involved are:

Location and proximity. Bare land prices have risen sharply in the last two decades. What once was an affordable quarter-acre or half-acre lot has now surpassed the average cost per square foot of acreage from just a decade ago.

Material prices. Materials needed for residential construction, like lumber, sheetrock, wood sheeting, and more, still display price instability even after the coronavirus pandemic of 2020. Although there may be dips in the inflated costs of these raw materials, the mean or median costs for goods have not receded to pre-pandemic pricing.

Finishes in the dwelling. People's tastes and standards for the finishes within their homes have become more luxurious than a decade ago when home finishes were very budget-friendly. In today's world of granite, stainless steel, home theaters, and golf simulators, many options in a new home can increase the final price.

Standard home plans versus custom plans. Traditional home plans are just what they're stated to be — conventional and likely without too many architectural features or efficient features in the home. Although standard home plans were pretty well the norm for the post-war era of the 1940s through the 1970s, these homes were built to withstand decades and were also made with plain features.

Standard house plans are drawn with the budget-minded buyer in mind and usually carry an affordable price tag that features box-like rooms, minimal restrooms, plain finishes and fixtures, sub-grade to mid-grade windows, and more.

Alternately, custom homes are designed by the homeowner through communication with the home builder regarding nearly every aspect of the home's rooms, layouts, flow, size of restrooms, and more. These types of homes that are built can become very expensive right from the start, as a custom-built home must have blueprints created with the new homeowner's customizations — which come with a hefty price tag.

A residential home estimator's processes and methods might differ distinctly from a commercial or industrial workflow. Simply by nature, the sector you are an estimator for determines the workflow and the majority of the elements of your estimate.

Here's an example of the typical cost elements of a residential home.

Pre-construction costs. Pre-construction costs in the residential sector can comprise 15 to 25% of the total construction cost. Within this 15-25% are costs such as the design of the house (which would include standard or custom plans), creating an initial budget or estimate, the land purchase and associated costs with the real estate transaction, permitting, and utility installation if no utilities are already onsite.

The actual costs of construction. Let's assume you've done your diligence with pre-construction and are now ready to calculate the cost of building the dwelling unit. You'll likely estimate or budget the project at a ratio of 50% materials and 50% labor, depending on the skill level of the available workforce. Within this skeleton building that won't be calculated with any finishes, you'll likely figure a certain percentage of the overall cost for the footings and foundation.

After the foundation costs are calculated, you'll need to start figuring out what the framing of the building will cost, and depending on the size of the house and the floor plan, it could range from $20,000 to upwards of $50,000.

After the framing costs are evaluated, you'll need to figure out one of the most expensive elements of new home construction – mechanical systems. Plumbing, HVAC, and Electrical always make up the most significant expense in any construction project, as without these systems, people won't stay warm, they won't have fresh water to drink, and they can't charge their cell phones or turn any lights on.

Mechanical systems in a moderately sized residential home of 2,200 square feet can come in somewhere near $30,000. In contrast, in a custom home nearly double that size, the entire mechanical system could reach a price tag of $70,000 or more.

Interior Finishes. Although the mechanical systems in a new home come with a hefty price tag, that's still not the most expensive element of building a new home. Interior home finishes can fall into very minimal or costly price categories; inside a custom-built house, there are many options for finishes, and these are typically the "homeowner choice" items where the owner gets to pick out exactly what they want.

Interior finishes that can be chosen as either budget-friendly or very expensive are items like plumbing fixtures, cabinets, lighting, flooring, doors, windows, carpets, and more. Depending on the range of finishes the owner chooses, this can drive an estimate up, and sometimes well beyond an established budget created in the pre-construction phase.

Without a doubt, the single-family home sector of the residential construction market is seemingly repetitious and thus can be a good sector to use historical data to dial in on your estimating process. Simply calculating the historical costs of building the dwelling divided by the square feet of the house will provide you with a per-square-foot price of similar houses you will estimate. Once you have completed several projects, that database will grow, and your historical data will continue to help you refine your estimating methods and process.

A conversation I once had with a former colleague who struck out on his own and now has a successful business for constructing high-end new homes and high-end residential remodeling explained some of the mistakes he learned from early on when he first opened his business.

These are a few mistakes he learned from in his first few years after moving from commercial to residential construction.

Underestimating Costs. A common misstep in residential construction estimating is neglecting certain expenses. Contractors often omit permits, licensing fees, transportation, wasted materials, and cleanup fees. Failing to account for these in estimates can significantly impact profits upon project completion. A comprehensive list of potential costs should be meticulously examined to address this. This includes checking for hidden charges in vendor discounts, incorporating consultation fees, and ensuring a thorough budget that safeguards profitability.

Unforeseen Expenses. A common mistake is the absence of a budget for unforeseen expenses, leading to projects exceeding their financial limits. A contingency fund is essential to address unexpected costs like increased labor or unplanned materials. Overestimating rather than underestimating is prudent when budgeting for unforeseen expenses, ensuring the project stays on track without costly delays.

Overlooking Insurance. Some estimators overlook the critical aspect of insurance, exposing them to project risks. Inadequate insurance coverage can result in legal battles and jeopardize the entire project. Estimators should clearly understand different types of insurance, including worker's compensation, general liability, and builder's risk.

Shopping for competitive pricing ensures comprehensive coverage and mitigates potential financial pitfalls.

Market Rate Ignorance. Neglecting to research market rates poses a significant risk in residential construction cost estimation. Contractors may undercharge or overcharge without awareness of competitors' charges for similar services, impacting profits and reputation. Thorough research on labor and material costs, tool and equipment rentals, and staying informed about market trends ensures accurate quotes, fair pricing, and sustained competitiveness.

Permit Costs. Underestimating the cost of necessary permits is a costly error in residential construction estimates. Acquiring permits can substantially increase the total project cost. A diligent approach involves researching local laws, understanding permit requirements, and factoring these costs into estimates upfront. Ignoring permit expenses can lead to financial repercussions for both the contractor and the client.

By recognizing and rectifying these common mistakes, estimators can strengthen their construction estimates, providing a foundation for successful residential building projects and earning clients' trust through transparent and accurate budgeting.

COMMERCIAL CONSTRUCTION ESTIMATING

In commercial construction estimating, the foundation lies in understanding the unique requirements of diverse structures that serve essential functions in our communities. Commercial buildings are not just structures; they are the lifelines of businesses, providing spaces for operations, transactions, and client engagement. Hospitals and medical centers are crucial to our healthcare infrastructure and cater to the public's well-being. Schools shape the future for the next generations, and shopping centers are vibrant arenas where retail business commerce occurs. As we delve into the intricacies of estimating costs for projects like these, commercial construction has a distinct significance in contributing to the functionality and vitality of our communities.

Commercial construction can be classified as any of these types of projects:

- Restaurants
- Retail, Grocery Stores, Shopping Malls
- Medical Facilities
- Office Buildings
- Hotels and Lodging Facilities
- Institutional Buildings
- Industrial Structures
- Sports Facilities
- Schools
- Municipal buildings

Within each of these project types, specific factors can impact costs. Unlike residential construction, where historical data is very advantageous to refining your estimates in a relatively short amount of time, commercial construction is a bit of a different scenario.

Many factors are involved in a commercial construction project, which can help or hinder the bottom line of your project estimate if not adequately accounted for.

When estimating the cost of a commercial project, various elements come into play beyond the building type. These factors include the size of the land acquired, the building's location, necessary permits and legal processes, and the timing of project completion throughout the year. For instance, it will be much costlier to construct a building in the winter months when in a snowy and cold region versus a mild temperature winter season.

The cost estimates of a commercial building somewhat resemble those encountered in residential construction or home building. Your commercial building estimate includes costs such as the foundation, labor, materials, location (region), finishing and fixtures, design, major mechanical systems, utilities, permits/legal, and land. Throughout the construction process, opportunities to save money exist, so it's advisable to over-estimate and then discuss cost-effective options with the project owners to achieve the best estimate, which will hopefully win the bid.

Some distinct factors of each element of commercial construction are listed below.

Foundation. In commercial construction, one of the priciest components is the foundation. Since commercial buildings are often quite sizable, a considerable amount of concrete, rebar, and other structural materials is necessary. Moreover, the ground must be readied and dug out before pouring the foundation. If foundation work occurs during the rainy season or even in colder climates, the weather can impact your cost estimate as rain or cold weather delays may happen.

Skilled Labor. Labor costs for commercial projects are regularly miscalculated and likely due to fluctuations in skilled labor costs. There are two types of skilled labor — union (or organized) labor and non-union labor. Each labor type has distinct differences, and each has its benefits. Either type of labor is subject to mandated work stoppages, labor disputes, vacation days, or holidays, among other factors that can delay a project. Know your labor market, what the project schedule entails, and whether that schedule may be affected by labor interruptions.

Location of the building. The geographical location where a commercial building will be constructed matters regarding cost. Usually, building in rural areas is more expensive because you're dealing with the cost of commercial real estate, likely the inability to connect to municipal utilities. Rural areas typically take longer to receive material or equipment deliveries than populated areas.

Finishes and fixtures. The estimated costs of building a commercial space include finishes and fixtures, and they can make a big difference. Going for higher-end finishes and fixtures will up the cost, while more budget-friendly options are available. Cheaper finishes might not last as long or be as good in quality. It's a good idea to find a middle ground and possibly discuss with the general contractor or whoever you are creating the estimate for bidding to talk about some value engineering options that might bring the cost down.

Engineering and Design. When estimating a commercial space, you'll need an architect or engineer to collaborate with the builder on the design. Typically, estimators are not engineers; crafting building designs takes time and money. A smart way to save money is to team up with a builder who has a designer or engineer. This not only saves you cash but also speeds up the process.

Mechanical System and Utilities. The major systems in your commercial building include plumbing, electrical, and HVAC (heating, ventilation, and air conditioning). When installed in a commercial setting, these systems must meet commercial standards. Commercial-grade mechanical and utility systems often come with an overall price increase, depending on the construction project's size and geographical region.

Land Purchase, Zoning, and Permits. Dealing with permits and legal matters is a must for commercial building projects and comes with a fee. A typical commercial construction project will have many permits, including building, electrical, plumbing, roofing, etc. Another significant expense is the land for your project, which typically wouldn't be included in the overall commercial building cost or the project you may be estimating. Land purchases and adjustments or revisions to the local zoning ordinances are typically settled long before you will be asked to create a pre-construction estimate.

As we've learned in this chapter, whether you're estimating in the residential or commercial sectors, putting together an in-depth and accurate construction estimate is a time-consuming process that requires a high degree of skill, knowledge, and technical expertise.

As you move forward in your estimating career, each time you perform a takeoff, assign labor hours or labor dollars to your estimate, gather your vendor material quotes, calculate your equipment rentals or costs, and add the multitude of additional cost factors that need to be accounted for, you are gaining knowledge, experience, and confidence in yourself as an estimator.

I explain many times in the book that you need consistency in your workflow, which will subconsciously help you gain the confidence to trust yourself and your methods in estimating. Think of it like this: if you haven't ridden a bicycle in several years, could you simply hop onto a bicycle and pedal away? The answer is likely yes, and this is the consistency and confidence I'm talking about.

We've all likely spent the hours and hours it may have taken as a child to learn how to keep that bicycle upright and in forward motion. We surely had mishaps along the way and maybe had a skinned knee or two, but we eventually figured out the subconscious process to keep the bicycle upright and move forward to get where we wanted to go. Venturing into the construction estimating world is no different than the bicycle analogy. We have to learn the methods and processes to stay upright (or profitable) on a construction project, and our forward motion (consistency) will get us to the next project, and the next, and so on.

In the next chapter, we will discuss how communication can affect a construction estimate and the overall bidding process and ultimately affect the probability of you securing the contract for the project.

5

COMMUNICATION AND COLLABORATION IN ESTIMATING

AS AN ESTIMATOR, arriving at the correct cost estimate is critical to a successful project. But it's not just the right estimating tools or software that will get us there; it's also working together as a team to win the project that plays a huge role in our success. When cost estimators, contractors, architects, and engineers team up, it boosts the accuracy and efficiency of takeoff and estimating. This chapter will take us through how and why collaboration matters so much in construction and how it makes construction projects more successful overall.

Some construction estimators strictly stay in the realm of estimating, meaning that the majority of what they do is "strip" plans, calculate the takeoffs, run some reports if using a software-based estimating system, and then hand off the estimating packet to a senior estimator or a project manager to review the estimate and start putting the final bid package together.

Alternatively, there are construction estimators who could be called "cradle-to-grave" estimators. Cradle-to-grave estimators are a one-stop shop of sorts as an estimator, a project manager, the point of contact for General Contractors, the person who calculates the monthly progress payments, and more.

In either scenario of your estimating position, you will need to communicate, communicate again, and communicate some more with your internal team at your place of employment and outside of your organization with project principles. These project principles can be the selected General Contractor, owners, stakeholders, or anyone with a financial vested interest in the project.

EFFECTIVE COMMUNICATION

Communication is imperative for an accurate estimate and, ultimately, a valid final bid to win a project. Listed below are key communication points that should regularly be discussed amongst all parties involved in creating the final bid documents.

Comprehending The Project Scope: Working together helps everyone understand exactly what the project needs. When everyone involved is part of the conversation from the start, everyone gets a clear picture of the project, its specifications, and its goals. Architects and engineers can share insights into the design, while contractors and estimators can pitch in with their know-how about construction and costs. With this shared understanding, the process of figuring out how much is needed and estimating costs becomes more accurate, lowering the chances of mistakes.

Removing Communication Barriers: Working together removes the hurdles in communication between different project teams. When communication flows better, everyone stays in the loop about any changes or updates that could affect figuring out how much is needed and estimating costs. Having regular meetings and coordination sessions and using communication tools that help everyone work together make it easier to talk openly and share ideas. This leads to a more accurate and efficient process for estimating.

Utilizing The Knowledge of Others: When people work together, they bring in different skills from various parts of a construction project. Estimators can learn a lot from architects, engineers, and contractors. They get insights into what materials are available, how things are installed, and what challenges might come up. All this shared knowledge helps estimators make more accurate calculations by considering the project's specific needs and limits. That leads to more precise cost estimates.

Feedback and Real-time Validation: When people collaborate and work together, estimators can get feedback and confirmation from architects, engineers, and general contractors immediately as they figure out costs. This quick feedback loop helps catch any mistakes, differences, or possible problems early on so they can be revised. Using the team's combined knowledge, estimators can ensure their calculations match the project's design, how it's being built, and the budgetary limitations.

Managing your risk: Working together is imperative in lowering risks when creating a cost estimate. When a multitude of people are part of the process, they can spot and deal with possible issues like not having enough materials, design conflicts, or logistics challenges. By taking action early to manage these risks, estimators can make better guesses about costs, reducing the chances of going over budget or delaying the schedule. The team's combined effort helps handle uncertainties, ensuring project planning and decisions are aligned with the project's expected outcome.

Why Relationships Matter: Working together builds trust and a friendly atmosphere among everyone involved in a project. When estimators talk and work closely with architects, engineers, and contractors, it creates a collaborative mindset where everyone respects and understands each other. This way of collaborating strengthens relationships, promotes teamwork, and improves the whole project. Estimators become trusted partners, appreciated for what they know and how they contribute to making the project successful.

As we've learned from these effective communication tactics, working together is essential for getting the correct cost estimates right from the start of construction projects. When everyone involved is part of the conversation, using their specific know-how and talking openly, estimators can effectively provide the costs for construction projects. Collaboration also helps lower risks, make better decisions, and create trust within the project team. Communication is key for construction professionals who want to do a great job estimating and ensuring the whole project succeeds.

THE VALUE OF COLLABORATION

To foster effective and collaborative communication between all parties involved in the bidding process, the first step is ensuring everyone sees the whole project the same way. The best way to do this is by giving access to models or documents that show all the details to the right people at the right time. Whether you're an architect, estimator, engineer, detailer, fabricator, or project manager, connecting your work and having one central place for information is essential. This helps everyone understand the big picture and the specific tasks that need to be done.

Access to the same real-time information from the pre-construction documents makes the construction process smoother and conversations with the team and others more helpful. Connecting different people early in the project improves understanding and lets everyone make better decisions for design and construction. When everyone involved is on the same page, connected, and working together, it leads to a better project and lowers risks. Strong collaboration means everyone in the project team is involved and ready to contribute their skills and knowledge to reach the goals together.

Suppose you've already been involved in construction, or if you're brand new, you'll soon realize the construction industry is a mix of different professionals and experts, making working together a bit tricky. There's a problem where each group involved in a project keeps their information separate, and this has been an issue for a long time. Unfortunately, this way of working is still common because there haven't been effective alternatives until the past decade when digital changes became possible.

Building a construction project with this 'separate information' mindset leads to a messy process. Because of tight schedules and changes that aren't documented well, the design work can end up with unclear parts that become mistakes and missing info in the construction plans. This can cause omissions on an estimate, and unforeseen costs can lead to expensive fixes and do-overs.

Another problem in the construction industry is how competitive it is. If a team has to compete to make a small profit and get the next job, they might focus more on finishing their part quickly and moving on to the next project instead of thinking about long-term goals. Delays, conflicts, and disagreements often make collaborating hard in this competitive setting.

Here are some benefits that result from effective communication and collaboration in construction.

Team Alignment and Shared Understanding. Working together helps everyone on the team, as estimators, subcontractors, and stakeholders, get on the same page. It ensures everyone knows what needs to be done and how each task affects the workflow. The best collaboration lets design experts mix their ideas with the practical know-how of fabricators, contractors, and other field team members.

An Effective Information Highway. In construction projects, many team members and partners simultaneously work on the same project at the same time, possibly in different locations. Sometimes, they can't find important information quickly and spend too much time looking for answers. Without the correct information, they won't have the proper understanding. Not having clear insights from an excellent pre-construction project model can lead to repeating the same work, making mistakes, misunderstandings, and wasting time. These problems can potentially cost money.

Collaboration is the solution – it lets you access information and share insights to make decisions with others involved. Bringing everyone together helps avoid surprises that can be expensive. For example, working together early can help find and fix issues before construction starts. Collaboration also reduces revisions to work already performed, often when planning is misjudged, and there are communication deficiencies.

Engagement and Accountability. When you are on the bid team for a construction project that shares tasks, and everyone seemingly works well together, everyone wants to do a great job and not disappoint others. Each team member should believe they can reach their common goal together. When team members communicate effectively and perform their part of the process well, everyone feels more confident and committed. If everyone involved in a project collaborates, talks effectively, and works together smoothly, it leads to the best possible outcome.

Educated Decision Making. Occasionally, some construction estimating professionals don't have full access to the data needed to improve the bidding process and, ultimately, the project. Collaboration is the starting point to give all team members the power to get the correct information and see the overall picture – like project schedules, deadlines, project cost conflicts, budget, and equipment needs. Information is powerful. When everyone can access the full scope of available information and work together, each person or team can understand and discuss the details with everyone involved in the bidding process. This way, they can voice their opinions and affect the design and production plan.

Collaboration Enhances Safety. Construction companies deal with tight schedules and challenging tasks when each part works separately. Planning these tasks without coordinating with other project partners can make the work less safe. A crucial step to make the site safer is ensuring everyone involved understands the project better and improves how they work with each other. Collaboration lets project estimators, project managers, and project stakeholders talk clearly about project concerns, conflicts on site, and safety risks. Clear communication about safety issues reduces confusion, clarifies expectations, and protects the expected profit margins on correctly estimated construction projects. When everyone openly discusses project concerns or successes, the key players on construction projects can lower risks and solve problems together early.

Throughout this chapter, we've learned that although there are many moving parts of a construction project, effective communication and regular collaboration with everyone involved in completing that project effectively work as a unified construction team. A team that is fully aware and educated on the project costs, deliverables, and expected outcomes will be a successful team that wins the contract for a project.

If everyone does their part and communicates, collaborates, and shares the information with the entire team, everyone will benefit from a profitable construction project you created the estimate for.

As this subtopic closes, in the simplest terms I can give you — communicating and collaboration in estimating essentially means that people are teaming up to achieve a common project goal. Everyone can quickly get a project's main plans and goals anytime, without needing gatekeepers or traveling to other companies' offices for information.

With solid collaboration, team members combine their resources and knowledge, focusing on achieving goals set by the project timeline and budget rather than individual objectives. This is the ideal approach to building construction projects.

PRESENTING YOUR ESTIMATE

Effective presentation of construction estimates is critical to the overall construction estimating process. Once a construction estimate is prepared, it needs to be communicated clearly and persuasively to various stakeholders involved in the project. This consists of conveying the estimated costs, timelines, and resource requirements in an easily understandable manner that aligns with the project's objectives. The presentation of your estimate serves as a means of securing approval and funding and as a tool for fostering collaboration and ensuring a shared understanding among team members and decision-makers.

Collaboration in construction estimating is greatly enhanced when estimates are presented transparently and comprehensively. Stakeholders, including project managers, architects, engineers, and financiers, benefit from a clear breakdown of costs and a visual representation of the project plan. Collaborative construction estimating platforms and tools facilitate effective communication, enabling stakeholders to discuss, refine, and align their expectations. The presentation of estimates thus becomes a key component in fostering collaboration and ensuring the success of construction projects.

Before presenting your estimate to a team or an individual, you must ensure you have a complete understanding of the elements of your estimate. *How do you effectively convey the information in those elements so no questions go unanswered?*

Here is a list of elements that must be crystal clear as you present your estimate.

Tools and Methods. Depending on your project's type and size, various methods and tools are available for estimating costs. Standard methods include unit cost, assembly cost, square foot, parametric, and cost index. Each technique has pros and cons, so selecting the one that aligns with your project and the data at your disposal is crucial. Utilizing dependable and up-to-date sources of information, such as cost databases, historical data, market surveys, or expert opinions, is essential. Additionally, employing software applications, spreadsheets, or project-specific calculators can aid in organizing, calculating, and presenting your estimate efficiently.

A Full Understanding of the Scope. Before commencing the estimation process, it is crucial to grasp the scope and specifications outlined in the project documents. This involves thoroughly examining drawings, plans, contracts, and other relevant materials delineating project requirements, goals, and expectations. Identifying assumptions, exclusions, contingencies, and potential risks that might impact the estimate is equally important. A comprehensive understanding of the project's scope and specifications helps prevent oversights, duplications, errors, and potential disputes in later stages of the project.

Offer Value Engineering Options. Optimizing your estimate and providing enhanced value to your client can be achieved by applying two techniques: value engineering and life cycle costing. Value engineering entails exploring alternative approaches to attain the same or improved functionality at a reduced cost, all while maintaining quality, safety, and performance standards. On the other hand, life cycle costing involves estimating the total cost of owning and operating a facility or system throughout its useful life, encompassing construction, maintenance, operation, and disposal expenses. Life cycle costing may be complex to gauge as an estimator unless you are continually involved with the project stakeholders after construction. Implementation of these techniques not only minimizes waste, but also enhances efficiency, and promotes sustainability.

Validate Your Estimate: After completing your estimate, conducting a thorough review and validation before presenting it to your client or stakeholder is essential. The review process involves checking for your estimate's completeness, consistency, accuracy, and clarity. Utilizing checklists, formulas, or software tools can aid in identifying and rectifying any errors or omissions. Validation, on the other hand, requires comparing your estimate with other sources of information like similar projects, industry benchmarks, or independent estimates. Seeking feedback from peers, supervisors, or experts can further validate and enhance the accuracy of your estimate.

Present Your Estimate. Presenting your estimate to your team, client, or stakeholder requires a professional approach. This involves creating a clear and concise report that encapsulates critical elements of your estimate, including scope, specifications, methods, assumptions, exclusions, contingencies, risks, and results. Supporting documents such as drawings, calculations, quotations, or references should be included. Effective communication of your estimate involves using suitable formats, charts, graphs, or tables. Additionally, explaining your estimate logically, confidently, and respectfully is crucial in addressing any questions or concerns arising during the presentation.

This chapter taught us that communication and collaboration are nearly as crucial to estimating as the estimate itself. Excellent communication ensures everyone involved in the bidding process is fully engaged and educated about every project detail.

When everyone communicates on the project, the result can only be positive outcomes that will position you and your estimate as the frontrunner on bid day.

Next, we will look at some estimating strategies that will help you in your everyday due diligence as an estimator.

Your Voice Can Be The Inspiration For Estimators Everywhere!

"You can use an eraser on the drafting table or a sledgehammer on the construction site." – Frank Lloyd Wright

Have you ever driven down the highway and noticed the massive amount of houses or buildings? Or, maybe you've been on vacation and marveled at a towering skyscraper poking into the clouds? *Do you know how these buildings came to be?*

Construction Estimators - that's how!

In *Construction Project Estimating 101,* I share my experiences to equip you with the hands-on insights needed for success. My goal is to provide a solid foundation for your journey in construction estimating.

I humbly request your help to reach thousands like you seeking this foundation. Your help will take less time than it takes to brew a cup of coffee, and can be done from the comfort of your own home! I simply request you leave a short review on Amazon.

Your review ensures that newcomers to the construction estimating world can easily discover the full potential for their career through 'Construction Project Estimating 101.'

Online reviews validate the usefulness of a product, and a brief sentence or two can have a real impact.

Think of how many product reviews you've read over the years; weren't they helpful?

Considering the challenges of finding tried and true information online about construction estimating, your voice is invaluable.

Thank you so much for your support. Your review is vital, and I appreciate your HONEST Amazon review tremendously.

Be the voice for 'Construction Project Estimating 101' for future estimators so they too can have this invaluable information in their estimating toolkit!

Simply scan the QR code to leave your review on Amazon!

6

ADVANCED ESTIMATING STRATEGIES

THROUGHOUT THE BOOK, we've covered many construction estimating processes and methods. One method I keep referencing is using estimating software as one of your primary methods. Plausibly, you may be an estimator who does their job the 'old school' way, using just a scale rule, a calculator, and pencil and paper.

If that's the case, good for you! You are definitely diving head-first into your position, as thousands of estimators have done before you for decades. Hopefully, this chapter will enlighten you more about the efficiencies available to construction estimators that considerably improve their workflow and overall estimating capabilities by using nearly failsafe software programs.

Conventional cost estimation methods involve manual calculations using paper or spreadsheets, presenting challenges with their cumbersome nature and susceptibility to human errors. These semi-outdated approaches overlook essential factors like material price fluctuations, labor costs, and project-specific complexities. As a result, inaccurate cost estimation may lead to underbidding, resulting in losses or overbidding, jeopardizing the acquisition of potential projects and future clients.

Fortunately, technological advancements have transformed the construction industry, introducing innovative solutions to address these challenges.

Let's get into some cutting-edge cost-estimating tools that can notably improve profitability and increase your success in bidding.

BUILDING INFORMATION MODELING (BIM).

Building Information Modeling (BIM) is a complete method for making and handling information related to construction projects. Using an intelligent model supported by an online platform, BIM combines organized, diverse data from various fields to create a digital version of a structure throughout its existence – from initial planning and design to construction and ongoing operations. Here are some key points why using BIM software in your estimating workflow is beneficial.

Accuracy: With BIM's 3D models and combined data, estimators can create accurate cost estimates for different project parts.

Effective Collaboration: BIM encourages teamwork among everyone involved in the project. This helps coordinate different aspects, reduces issues, and improves cost estimates.

Managing Changes: BIM's updates in real-time make it easy to adjust costs quickly. This helps organizations adapt smoothly to any changes in the project.

ESTIMATING SOFTWARE PROGRAMS

Estimating software plays a crucial role in the construction industry, bringing about significant benefits in terms of efficiency and accuracy. These tools streamline the estimation process, replacing manual calculations and spreadsheet-based methods. By automating the computation of material quantities, labor costs, and project complexities, estimating software reduces the likelihood of human errors, ensuring more precise and reliable cost predictions. This saves valuable time and enhances the overall accuracy of project budgets, allowing construction professionals to make well-informed decisions based on solid financial data.

Incorporating estimating software into your daily routine promotes collaboration and communication among project stakeholders. These solutions provide a centralized platform where architects, engineers, contractors, and subcontractors can collectively contribute to the estimation process. Real-time collaboration fosters interdisciplinary coordination, reduces conflicts, and ensures that all team members are on the same page regarding cost-related aspects of the project. This improved communication leads to more accurate and holistic estimations, ultimately contributing to the success of construction projects by minimizing the risk of underbidding or overestimating costs. Estimating software solutions empowers the construction industry to work more efficiently, make informed financial decisions, and deliver projects within budget and on schedule.

The efficiencies provided by software-based estimating programs mean that as an estimator, your takeoffs will be more consistent and with increased accuracy. Nearly every function of a computerized estimating program is digitized, whether it's counting, tracing the building outline to establish the accurate building square footage, and providing a bill of materials (or a material list) that is accurate based on your inputs into the program.

What I have found incredibly useful over the past fifteen or so years of using computer-based estimating programs is that the computer mouse you use is imperative to keeping good hand and wrist health. While using these estimating programs, you constantly move the mouse, click the mouse button, drag lines across the blueprint on the screen, or click hundreds of points on the blueprint if you perform a quantity takeoff for a single item.

For context on this topic, I am oftentimes at my computer for an entire day, stripping plans on very large, complex projects that sometimes take multiple weeks to perform the entire takeoff, sheet by sheet, with the blueprint on my screen.

In my estimating career, I have tried at least a half-dozen computer 'mice' until I found one that works effectively for me. Some of these trials may have taken a few weeks to get a good feel for the mouse and whether it would work for me, and if it didn't work - I would return the mouse and move on to the next one to try.

Given that my estimating career has primarily been on the mechanical side of construction, after many trials and errors, I finally arrived at a device that remains stationary on my desk, meaning the mouse doesn't move. There is a roller ball under my thumb, and the traditional left and right mouse buttons are placed where you'd typically expect the buttons to be on a conventional mouse.

The rollerball mouse was advantageous for me as I would not feel the shoulder or elbow discomfort as with a conventinal mouse, my arm was moving around my desk constantly trying to pull lines across a blueprint. These lines are the pipes I trace out on the blueprint on my screen. The rollerball mouse lets me keep my hand stationary on my desk and allow my thumb to do most of the scrolling on the screen to trace piping, indicate where I have a counted item, and zoom in and out on the blueprint.

A rollerball-style mouse is the best device I've found that fits into my workflow and methods, even though I occasionally feel slight discomfort in my hand. After a long day of stripping plas, my thumb sometimes will need a good stretch by attempting to pull my thumb away from my forefinger as far as it will go.

As an estimator using software-based construction estimating programs, you must judge your hand health and be aware of the ramifications of ignoring what your computer mouse-driving hand is telling you. If you're aware of your hand health and new to software-based estimating, you'll quickly understand that by using an E-takeoff program, you will become far more efficient, which means more estimates, which then, in turn, means more projects bid and won. Ignoring the signs of hand fatigue while using these programs is not smart estimating, as you're setting yourself up for further problems down the road.

A bit later in the book, we will take a deep dive into some computer estimating software programs and their capabilities.

THE INFLUENCE OF ARTIFICIAL INTELLIGENCE

The slow adoption of new technologies in construction is particularly evident in the laborious construction cost estimation process. Obtaining final price estimates for a single project may take weeks or even months, resulting in unnecessary spending of precious revenue solely to mobilize for the preconstruction process. This ineffective up-front cost scenario highlights the industry's need for technological advancements to streamline processes and enhance efficiency.

Fortunately, adopting AI estimating software to expedite the takeoff process has returned positive outcomes for construction firms. Prominent global leaders in the construction sector claim that embracing this technology has allowed them to enhance efficiency and dedicate more attention to value-driven tasks such as scoping, pricing, and value engineering. This technological integration has not only boosted estimators' productivity but also elevated the precision of their takeoffs.

The consequential impact includes reduced preconstruction costs and the ability for firms to submit more competitive proposals, ultimately leading to heightened profitability.

Undoubtedly, AI is exerting a positive influence on diverse industries. In healthcare, it offers data-driven support to medical professionals by identifying patterns and delivering automated insights. This aids in tasks like medical records management, treatment, and digital consultations, streamlining workflows from routine activities to data management and drug creation.

The impact of AI extends seamlessly to agriculture, addressing the projected 2 billion increase in the world's population by 2050. As indicated by United Nations predictions, artificial intelligence and machine learning showcase the potential to meet the 60% rise in food productivity required to feed growing populations.

Pioneers like 'Amazon Go' leverage AI to introduce checkout-free stores in the retail sector. This technology allows customers to grab products from the shelf, exit the store, and have their Amazon account automatically handle the payment. Beyond eliminating the need to wait in line, AI provides insights into customer preferences, enabling retail brands to enhance customer experience based on data.

Given its transformative effects across various fields, the global AI market is valued at an estimated USD 136.6 billion as of 2022. Projections indicate that the value of the AI industry will surge over 13 times, reaching $1.81 trillion by 2030.

As the benefits of AI gain recognition across diverse industries, including healthcare, manufacturing, banking, and agriculture, its integration into the construction sector is steadily increasing. AI is beginning to revolutionize the processes involved in designing and constructing buildings. Its applications span various areas, including construction management, auditing, optimizing the preconstruction phase, AI-assisted takeoffs, cost estimation, architecture, interior design, and more.

Below, we will read how Artificial intelligence used in the construction industry is expected to have beneficial impacts within multiple construction areas.

Streamlining Repetitive Tasks. Machine intelligence can efficiently handle repetitive and tedious tasks like cost estimations, operating faster and tirelessly working 24/7. In contrast, the human brain tends to tire and lose focus after extended work hours, heightening the risk of errors and inaccuracies.

When properly maintained, intelligent machines remain unwavering in their focus, operating continuously without needing lunch breaks, sick days, or substantial wages. Despite the clear advantages of artificial intelligence, there is resistance to its adoption due to concerns about its potential impact on construction jobs.

However, the evidence suggests that AI will unlikely replace the human workforce entirely. Instead, it is poised to reshape and optimize the construction industry's business model. Beyond reducing costly errors, enhancing efficiency, and minimizing worksite injuries, the automation of repetitive tasks will empower teams and leaders to concentrate on value-generating activities with a more significant impact on profitability.

Reducing On-The-Job Injuries. The construction industry is recognized as one of the most hazardous employment sectors. AI-driven intelligent robots can be programmed to take over high-risk tasks, such as lifting heavy equipment and excavating in dangerous conditions. These robots can also be engineered to interact efficiently with their surroundings and operate autonomously in environments that pose risks.

Cost Control. Inaccurate cost estimates are a leading factor contributing to cost overruns. Traditional methods, whether manual or digitized, using rollers and rulers with a mouse for takeoffs and cost estimations, are still susceptible to human error.

The integration of artificial intelligence automates manual processes prone to human error, particularly in cost estimation. This not only enhances efficiency but also significantly improves accuracy. Consequently, the risk of cost overruns is reduced, ensuring profitability for the construction firm, subcontractors, and project owners.

Better Building Design. The 3D representation of a building needs to integrate architecture, engineering, mechanical, electrical, and plumbing (MEP) plans, along with the sequential activities performed by each team. The objective is to prevent conflicts among the models generated by various sub-teams. Industry experts are utilizing machine learning, specifically generative design, to identify and address clashes between models during the design phase. This proactive approach helps avoid the need for rework.

Enhanced Productivity. In the preconstruction phase, AI-enabled takeoffs outpace manual or digitalized methods, completing tasks within seconds rather than weeks or months, achieving an impressive 97% accuracy. This minimizes the risk of human error and allows estimators and general contractors to expedite proposal completion, gaining a competitive edge.

During implementation, construction firms are expected to enhance productivity by up to 50% through real-time data analysis. Consequently, many construction companies embrace AI and machine learning to optimize labor and machinery distribution across projects. Autonomous robots and AI-powered drones can identify worker locations, detect equipment, and assess job progress. This information empowers project managers to ensure sufficient workforce and equipment at job sites, preventing delays.

AI is just on the cusp of integrating into nearly every aspect of our daily lives. If you've ever verbally asked your smartphone a question, your smartphone AI answered your question. Suppose you've been discussing watching a movie with your friend, and the next day, you see a social media post about that same movie. It's plausible that AI was listening in and 'suggestively selling' that movie to you. If you subscribe to television streaming services and those services keep 'suggesting' movies or shows of the same genre, AI is listening.

Artificial Intelligence is here to stay, and the construction industry is not far from fully adopting its capabilities.

INCORPORATING RISK MANAGEMENT INTO ESTIMATES

Risk management constitutes a methodical procedure encompassing identifying, assessing, and controlling risks that could influence project objectives. As it applies to cost estimating, this entails scrutinizing potential uncertainties that might impact project costs and formulating preemptive strategies to handle them. Individuals and companies adopting a proactive stance towards risk management are poised to make more informed decisions and ensure their profitability on construction projects.

Below are some key areas to consider for your risk management control within your estimates.

Identify and Assess Your Risk Factors. The initial risk management phase involves pinpointing potential factors impacting project costs. These risks may emanate from various origins, such as market conditions, disruptions in the supply chain, regulatory shifts, unforeseen events, and latent site conditions. Engaging stakeholders, design consultants, and project teams in this process ensures a comprehensive identification of risks, incorporating diverse perspectives.

Following the identification of risks, the subsequent stage is their assessment to gauge their potential influence on project costs. This entails scrutinizing each risk occurrence's likelihood and estimating the magnitude of its consequences. Such an evaluation aids in prioritizing risks based on their significance, allowing project teams and owners to allocate resources and attention judiciously.

Address Your Risks. Cost estimating risk management can be addressed through quantitative or qualitative methods or a blend of both. Quantitative approaches employ statistical techniques, historical data, and mathematical models to quantify the impact of risks on project costs precisely. On the other hand, qualitative methods lean on expert judgment, experience, and subjective assessments to qualitatively evaluate risks and their potential effects. The fusion of these methodologies results in a comprehensive risk management framework.

Mitigate, Monitor, and Adapt. The primary objective of risk management in cost estimation is to devise effective strategies for risk mitigation. These strategies are designed to diminish the likelihood or impact of identified risks and establish contingency plans if they materialize. Mitigation measures encompass engaging a quantity surveyor for cost management services, collaborating with experienced design consultants and contractors, diversifying suppliers or subcontractors, devising backup plans, integrating risk allowances (contingencies) in cost estimates, and implementing proactive monitoring and control mechanisms. Taking a proactive stance toward risks aids in minimizing cost overruns, delays, and other adverse impacts on project budgets.

Risk management is an ongoing and iterative process, not a singular activity. As projects progress and new risks surface, continuous monitoring and reassessment of identified risks become imperative. Routine updates to cost estimates (referred to as Cost Planning) should mirror the present risk landscape and incorporate necessary adjustments. This ensures the ongoing accuracy and relevance of cost estimates throughout the project's lifecycle.

Some risks are typical for most projects you estimate, which may vary depending on the sector you are estimating for. I've found that this list is pretty consistent throughout construction, and it's typically the minor details of each risk that may have a select set of variables.

This is a 'baseline' risk assessment list I check off for each estimate I perform.

- Project Schedule.
- Project Location.
- Safety Factors/Concerns.

- Subcontractor Performance.
- Material(s) Availability.
- Liquidated Damages.
- Performance Bonds.
- Contingencies.

By incorporating risk management processes into your estimates, you'll define the known risks and the impact those risks may have on the overall project. The impact from those risks may need to be identified as a monetary cost, depending on the risk, and that cost should be considered and provided for within your estimate.

UNFORESEEN CHALLENGES

Within construction, as an estimator, you should always prepare for the unexpected challenges that only a Genie with a crystal ball could accurately identify before starting a project.

You might have historical data for past projects at your fingertips, possibly dating back a decade — but that historical data cannot prepare you for every new project you are estimating, as every project has its own set of circumstances, potential delays, and unforeseen conditions that only unfold as the project progresses.

As you gain experience in your estimating career and start noticing little things here and there on the blueprints or buried in a specification book, you'll realize that you can identify the potential for the unforeseen. Still, it's usually improbable to predict these events.

Here's a list of some common unforeseen challenges that, although they are pretty typical from project to project, usually have distinctly different outcomes.

Project Management Errors. In construction projects, deficient scheduling, and project management issues can give rise to unanticipated costs stemming from subpar performance. This encompasses inadequate coordination among subcontractors, compromising the quality of work and contributing to accidents. Lack of effective communication results in errors and costly revisions, while insufficient inspections allow substandard performance to go unnoticed, necessitating expensive repairs. Poorly devised timelines lead to rushed work, delays, and heightened costs. Additionally, inadequate risk assessment leads to unforeseen complications that impact progress, quality, and the project budget.

Incorrect Project Design. Ineffective communication can result in design shortcomings, which are responsible for approximately 40% of construction disputes. This issue can give rise to cost overruns and inferior work quality and may even escalate into legal conflicts.

Communication Deficiencies. Achieving success in your construction project, staying within budget, and meeting client expectations becomes nearly impossible without open lines of communication among all parties involved.

Administrative Issues. Administration errors stand out as another prevalent factor behind unforeseen costs. Even minor mistakes have the potential to escalate into substantial expenses. Instances such as miscommunication in accounting, inadequate document management, and inappropriate micromanagement can collectively contribute to cost overruns.

Errors On The Estimate. Some companies rush to put together proposals in a competitive construction bidding marketplace. This decision can lead to inaccurate project estimates, including budgets and schedules that are inaccurate. Additionally, this rush to complete a bid might have been created using a generic approach in their estimate, increasing the chance of going over the initial budget and losing the project.

As a construction estimator, you must provide the team with the most complete, up-to-date final cost estimate. When creating an estimate, you must factor in many items discussed in this chapter and utilize those that benefit the sector or industry.

In the next chapter, we will begin analyzing some of the legal and ethical factors estimators may encounter and how to effectively plan, prepare, and account for those costs in your bid.

7

THE LEGAL AND ETHICAL SIDE OF CONSTRUCTION ESTIMATING

For construction estimating professionals, prioritizing ethics is crucial in every decision-making process. Job estimating is a susceptible area where ethical practices play a vital role.

Maintaining ethics in construction estimating is pivotal for fostering solid relationships with contractors and project owners. This ethical approach establishes trust and demonstrates a commitment to moral dealings with clients.

Adhering to ethical standards during estimating is a preventive measure against legal issues that contractors may encounter if ethics are not integrated into their pricing model. Let's dig deeper into how you can contribute to upholding ethics during the estimation stage.

FACTORS THAT AFFECT ETHICS

Before understanding the applied principles of ethics in construction estimating, examining factors influencing costs that may equate to shortcuts could lead to unethical estimating practices.

Labor Costs. Quality staff comes at a price, and cutting corners by hiring lower-quality workers can pose safety hazards and lead to additional expenses for redoing tasks on the job site, negatively impacting profitability.

Supply Costs. Inflation has significantly raised material prices, requiring adept negotiation with vendors to offer clients quality materials at a fair price while maintaining a profit. Regularly assessing material costs and seeking better deals ensures reasonable practices rather than compromising with subpar materials.

Unseen Costs. Permits, insurance, and other hidden expenses play a pivotal role in construction. While not visible on the job site, ethical estimation of these line items is essential to safeguard the client's best interests.

Once you understand these cost factors, exploring how to price a construction project ethically is vital, as the ethical tone established at the project's outset will resonate throughout its entirety.

Here are some great points on instilling the right ethical tone from the beginning.

Ethical From The Start. Well before the first foundation is laid or the initial nail is hammered, you will present an estimate to your team or the client. Although this preliminary estimate is typically not a legally binding contract, upholding ethical standards during this phase remains essential.

It is crucial to provide an estimate that aligns with your genuine belief in your ability to meet it. Engaging in underbidding solely to secure a project and increasing costs after contract signing is considered unethical.

Instances abound of construction companies facing legal challenges due to quoting one price to a client and then raising it after the project commencement. Once plans are in motion and the project is underway, clients find it challenging to terminate contracts and initiate anew, leaving them feeling constrained by an agreement they did not consent to.

Underbidding Labor Calculations. Compensating your crew fairly is not just an ethical consideration; it's a legal imperative. Additionally, it presents an opportunity to enhance your reputation as a reputable construction firm.

Depending on the job's pricing structure, you may have an arrangement enabling you to pass labor costs to the client throughout the project's duration. It is crucial to avoid inflating time sheets to maximize profits.

Employing skilled workers is vital, as opting for unskilled labor to cut costs can result in safety concerns, rework, and negative publicity for the project and possibly you as the estimator. Always prioritize what is in the best interest of your bid team.

Ethically Source Materials. Operating ethically when handling materials is imperative. Estimating a job's cost based on high-quality materials and subsequently using lower-grade materials is highly unethical and potentially illegal.

Clients who consent to a price based on top-notch materials can take legal action against your firm if they discover the use of substandard materials. Furthermore, once a written commitment is made to procure materials from a specific vendor, it is illegal to seek cheaper alternatives elsewhere.

Construction estimating poses a formidable challenge for all parties involved in the construction process, with many factors to consider. Amidst potential pressures to manipulate your estimate to cheat the system in favor of your company, it is crucial to maintain a steadfast focus on supporting your desire to win the contract through ethical dealings.

Regrettably, unethical practices are prevalent in many businesses, with contractors and the construction industry often bearing the brunt of such perceptions. Unfortunately, some contractors engage in unethical behavior; however, it is equally true that some clients also partake in unfair practices, withholding payments rightfully due to contractors. It is important to note that not all contractors or clients are unethical, and a broad generalization should be avoided.

LEGAL COMPLIANCE IN ESTIMATING

Legal compliance holds the utmost significance in construction estimating for several compelling reasons. First, eligibility for public projects, especially those funded by government entities, mandates contractors to meet specific legal requirements. Non-compliance with these requisites may lead to disqualification from bidding on lucrative public projects.

Beyond eligibility considerations, adherence to legal requirements is pivotal in risk mitigation. This includes averting potential legal disputes, fines, or project delays. Contractors and estimators who conform to laws and regulations safeguard their reputations and ensure financial stability.

Furthermore, legal compliance becomes a decisive factor in winning contracts. Contractors with a proven track record of adhering to legal requirements are more likely to secure bids. Clients prioritize contractors exhibiting reliability, professionalism, and a commitment to project specifications, making legal compliance a key attribute in the competitive bidding landscape.

Many considerations can be made for staying on the right side of the illegalities of construction estimating, contracting, and construction as a whole.

Below are some key takeaways to ensure you always remain legally in compliance.

Project Requirements and Specifications. Before submitting a bid for any construction project, a meticulous review of all project requirements and specifications is imperative. This encompasses a thorough understanding of the legal obligations articulated in the bidding documents, which may include licenses, permits, insurance, and certifications. Non-compliance with these stipulations could lead to immediate disqualification.

Key Takeaway: Conducting a comprehensive assessment of project requirements is crucial for ensuring that contractors are well-prepared to meet legal obligations, thereby minimizing the risk of non-compliance.

Licensing and Certifications. Securing and upholding the requisite licenses, certifications, and registrations is a foundational element of legal compliance in construction bidding. It is incumbent upon contractors to verify that they possess the necessary permits or licenses mandated by local, state, and federal laws. These may encompass trade-specific licenses, general contractor licenses, or certifications attesting to compliance with particular safety standards.

Key Takeaway: The meticulous upkeep of appropriate licensing and certifications signifies a contractor's dedication to legal compliance, bolsters their credibility, and increases the likelihood of winning bids.

Labor Laws. Maintaining legal compliance in the bidding process necessitates strict adherence to employment and labor laws. Contractors must comply with wages, working hours, benefits, and occupational safety regulations. Understanding these laws is crucial to avoid potential penalties, lawsuits, or harm to the contractor's reputation.

Key Takeaway: Strict adherence to employment and labor laws ensures ethical practices and promotes worker safety, reducing the risk of legal disputes and safeguarding the contractor's reputation.

Environmental Compliance. Environmental compliance is imperative in construction projects due to their potential significant impacts. Contractors must strictly adhere to laws governing handling hazardous materials, waste disposal, and environmental conservation. Non-compliance can result in severe consequences, including fines, project delays, or legal action.

Key Takeaway: Compliance with environmental regulations underscores a contractor's dedication to sustainable practices. This commitment enhances their reputation and instills trust in clients, potentially contributing to winning bids.

Successfully navigating the intricacies of legal compliance in construction bidding is crucial for contractors aiming for success in the industry. Appreciating the significance of legal compliance, conducting thorough reviews of project requirements, upholding necessary licenses and certifications, strict adherence to employment and labor laws, and considering environmental regulations are pivotal strategies. Employing these measures enhances contractors' prospects of securing contracts and thriving in the competitive landscape of today's construction market.

RESOLVING DISPUTES

Regarding dispute resolution within the construction industry, mediation has emerged as a valuable alternative to traditional litigation or arbitration. Diverging from approaches that pit two sides against each other, mediation fosters collaboration and negotiation to attain mutually agreeable solutions.

Central to mediation is the involvement of a neutral third party, the mediator, who facilitates communication among all disputing parties. This voluntary and confidential process encourages open dialogue, allowing each party to articulate concerns and explore potential solutions.

The benefit of mediation is that it resolves a construction dispute instead of litigation, which is the best option for all parties. Mediation operates to bring both parties to an agreeable resolution in which each party agrees to the negotiated terms of the resolution.

The benefits of mediation far outweigh the alternative of one party suing the other, and here are the reasons why.

Efficiency. Mediation is known for its prompt resolution, taking less time than the lengthier litigation or arbitration processes. This efficiency is particularly crucial in the construction industry, where timely dispute resolution is essential.

Cost-effectiveness. In contrast to the high legal fees and extended court proceedings associated with litigation, mediation offers a more affordable option for resolving construction disputes, reducing financial burdens.

Preserving relationships. The primary aim of mediation is to sustain working relationships between parties, fostering goodwill and maintaining ongoing partnerships. This aspect is essential in the construction industry, where collaboration among stakeholders is often vital for future projects.

Flexibility. Mediation allows parties to craft solutions tailored to their unique needs and objectives. Unlike a judge or arbitrator dictating the outcome, the parties play a central role in determining the resolution.

Confidentiality. Mediation ensures confidentiality, creating a secure environment where parties can freely express themselves without concerns about damaging their reputation or negatively impacting future business opportunities.

By strategically incorporating mediation and upholding best practices, the construction industry can efficiently navigate dispute resolution, fostering transparency, collaboration, and fairness. The judicious use of mediation expedites conflict resolution and mitigates the potential adversarial consequences associated with prolonged litigation or arbitration. This approach ensures that disputes are handled with a focus on preserving working relationships, a vital aspect in an industry where collaboration among stakeholders often lays the groundwork for future projects.

Embracing best practices in dispute resolution through mediation underscores a commitment to ethical conduct and legal compliance. It reflects a proactive stance in addressing conflicts, promoting open communication, and seeking mutually agreeable solutions. This contributes to the integrity of construction estimating processes and enhances the industry's reputation for moral and responsible business practices.

Ultimately, the successful implementation of mediation and adherence to best practices safeguard working relationships and contribute significantly to the overall success of construction projects. The construction industry establishes a foundation for sustained growth, client satisfaction, and enduring partnerships by prioritizing ethical considerations and legal compliance in dispute resolution.

In the upcoming chapter, we will learn how construction estimators can further their estimating methods and processes through additional education opportunities and developing advanced estimating skills.

8

THE FUTURE OF CONSTRUCTION ESTIMATING

In the construction world, new estimators must keep their finger on the pulse of the future for construction methods and tactics. As we enter a new decade, understanding the upcoming trends is more important than ever. This chapter explores the changes happening in construction, giving valuable insights into new ways of constructing, contemporary materials that are cheaper and more sustainable, and new estimating methods to add to your estimating toolkit. The future will significantly shift how we assess costs, from new technologies to eco-friendly practices.

It's essential to grasp the key factors influencing construction to succeed in the next ten years. The following pages explain how green energy, technology, and market changes impact construction projects.

This chapter will enlighten you about the adopted construction trends that are not far off from being an everyday reality.

A CHANGING CONSTRUCTION LANDSCAPE

According to Global Management Consulting firm McKinsey & Company, construction is the largest industry in the world. Yet, it makes up only about 13% of global GDP and is also one of the slowest growing. However, new construction technologies are looking to speed up the rate of change.

There are changes on the horizon in construction, which will affect how you create estimates. Some of these changes are already in use, although not widely seen - while other changes are just picking up their pace.

Modular and Prefabricated Construction. Modular construction typically involves building 60-90% of a structure before bringing it to the site. Prefabrication, a part of modular construction, happens when specific components are made off-site and later attached to the building.

As of 2022, the global modular construction market is valued at around $91 billion and is expected to reach $120.4 billion by 2027. Modular construction has seen rapid growth despite being smaller than the overall construction market. McKinsey notes a 51% increase in North American permanent modular construction projects from 2015 to 2018, with total revenue more than doubling.

General contractors, architects, and developers increasingly use prefabrication and modular construction to cut costs, shorten timelines, and reduce waste. Dodge's 2020 report indicates that 90% of respondents find these methods more beneficial than traditional construction.

Certain types of buildings, particularly healthcare facilities, are expected to benefit the most from modular construction and prefabrication in the next three years. Hotels, motels, and multifamily residential structures are significant beneficiaries, with hotels and motels leading the way between 2018 and 2020.

Smart Cities. One major trend shaping the construction industry is the emergence of smart cities, fully integrated with the Internet of

Things (IoT). The infrastructure and buildings in these cities collect data to enhance efficiency.

Global spending on smart cities reached $124 billion in 2020, marking a nearly 20% increase from 2019. Industry analysts project that investments in smart cities will reach $203 billion by 2024, and some estimates suggest the market could double to over $676 billion by 2028. This growing concept is poised to transform the construction industry.

Construction professionals will increasingly need to embrace technological advancements like IoT in building materials. A recent study indicates that 60% of US building managers are familiar with IoT technology, and 43% anticipate its impact on their business in the coming years.

In anticipation of this shift, large corporations and cities are entering agreements to develop smart cities in the next year. For example, Toyota has announced a 2,000-person smart city outside of Tokyo. The company aims to test autonomous vehicles and "smart buildings" in a real-world environment with residents. Construction for this innovative project began in February 2021.

Green Building. Green building involves building environmentally sustainable buildings using an environmentally sustainable construction and design process. In North America, Mexico is expected to lead the way in adopting green building practices. More than half of Mexican builders anticipate that most buildings will be environmentally friendly.

The green building movement is gaining significant traction, especially in residential construction. Over one-third of current US builders working on single-family and multi-family projects use green building techniques for at least half of their projects.

When it comes to improving the environmental performance of homes, energy efficiency is considered the top practice by home builders. A striking 96% of builders focused on green homes prioritize energy efficiency in their construction.

This emphasis on energy efficiency is crucial because building operations contribute the most to greenhouse gas emissions in the construction and real estate sectors. Consequently, more than 90% of single-family residential builders use energy efficiency practices in constructing some of their buildings, with 69% using these practices in most projects.

Living Building Materials. A groundbreaking trend in the construction industry involves using living building materials, a clear choice when considering the environmental impact.

The construction supply chain contributes to 11% of global greenhouse gas emissions, and nearly 30% of these emissions in the construction and real estate sectors come from embodied carbon released during construction. With the construction of new buildings expected to grow, global building stock is projected to double by 2060.

The living material sector targets areas like cement, contributing to 8% of global CO2 emissions. To align with the Paris Agreement on climate change, emissions from this sector must decrease by 16% before 2030. The cement sector would be the third-largest carbon emitter after China and the US (if that sector was indeed considered a country).

Innovative products such as self-replicating concrete and self-mending biocement are being developed in response to these challenges. Biocement, grown using biological materials instead of non-renewable ones, reduces emissions and absorbs CO2. This shift allows for the growth of self-replicating building materials, offering a more efficient and scalable solution.

Construction Drones. The construction industry is enhancing efficiency by adopting drone technology, once considered novelty items but now instrumental in substantial cost savings on significant projects.

Drone usage is estimated to significantly reduce the annual $160 billion waste on construction sites. Real-time drone measurements of building material stockpiles have increased accuracy by 61%. There is optimism that drones will play a crucial role in minimizing construction worker injuries and fatalities.

In the US, where 20% of workplace deaths occur in the construction industry, accounting for 6% of the labor force, drones provide a safer alternative for surveying and inspecting locations without exposing humans to potential harm. As a result, the construction industry has experienced a notable 55% increase in safety standards.

A 2018 study by DroneDeploy, a drone cloud computing company, revealed that the construction industry adopted drone technology faster than any other sector.

Improving Construction Safety Using Technology. From 2011 to 2019, there was a 41% increase in fall-related injuries, and nonfatal injuries rose 8%. In 2022, over 395 people in the construction industry died from falls, slips, or trips, prompting a demand for improved safety equipment incorporating technology.

While hard hats have been a longstanding safety staple, there's a current "helmet revolution" in the industry. Safety helmets, like those worn in rock climbing, are gaining popularity for various reasons. They feature a chin strap to stay securely on a worker even during a fall, offer a broader field of vision, and provide a more compact, ergonomic fit.

Recent advancements in safety helmets aim to minimize impact and prevent head and neck injuries. HexArmor's helmet, for instance, incorporates a Kinetix suspension system that absorbs and directs impact away from the neck and spinal cord, reducing impact force by 40% more than other helmets. Some helmets, like those by twICEme technology, even integrate the user's medical and emergency contact information directly into the helmet using NFC technology, eliminating the need for GSM, wi-fi, or 3G/4G/5G communication.

Wearables are another tech-enabled safety trend on construction sites. Kenzen, a tech company focused on preventing industrial workforce injuries, has introduced a continuous health monitoring program for the construction industry. Workers wear a small device on their upper arm to monitor core body temperature, heart rate, sweat rate, and activity level. The data feeds into an app visible to the worker and the manager.

The Labor Shortage. The construction industry has been grappling with a labor shortage for several years, reaching a "crisis level" in 2022, as noted by the CEO of the Home Builders Institute. In April 2022, there were 494,000 open jobs in construction—a 40% increase from April 2021 and the highest total since tracking began in 2000.

Although job openings slightly decreased to 466,000 in May 2022, it still marked a 39% year-over-year increase, setting a record for May. The situation is expected to worsen with the influx of funds from the recent Infrastructure Investment and Jobs Act.

The Association of Builders and Contractors estimates that the industry must hire an additional 650,000 workers in the coming years to meet demand, impacting project timelines and completion rates. A survey revealed that 89% of construction firms struggle to fill positions, with 61% experiencing project delays due to the labor shortage.

The Home Builders Institute emphasizes that the scarcity of construction workers significantly contributes to the shortage of housing inventory and affordability. Almost 42% of the construction labor force is engaged in residential construction.

An industry analyst points out a 25% gap between unfilled positions and hires, anticipating increased project costs due to higher salaries.

The industry employs various strategies to address the shortage, such as early outreach programs in grade schools, promoting diversity in hiring, leveraging social media for recruitment, and offering retention bonuses.

One positive aspect is the 5% increase in enrollment in construction industry trades courses at community colleges between 2019 and 2022, in addition to a renewed push by the United States Government to educate young adults of high school age about the benefits of apprenticeship, and how a high school graduate can enter the construction workforce immediately out of high school.

Ongoing Supply Chain Issues. Numerous construction firms are grappling with challenges in obtaining certain materials, and even when available, the costs are surging. Over 90% of builders report facing shortages of materials, with a survey revealing that more than 70% of builders marked deficiencies in half of the presented items.

Data from June 2022 by the Associated General Contractors of America highlights a nearly 17% increase in prices for construction materials used in nonresidential projects since June 2021. Notably, construction inputs like diesel fuel (doubled since June 2021), asphalt roofing products (up 22% year-over-year), and plastic construction products (up 27% year-over-year) have witnessed significant price hikes.

The demand and cost for aluminum have also seen considerable growth, with a 7.7% increase in 2021 and an additional 5.3% surge in the first quarter of 2022. Aluminum prices have reached record highs, with an estimated average price-per-ton of $3,450 in 2022.

Steel, another essential material, faces scarcity and rising costs. The Bureau of Labor Statistics Producer Price Index indicated a 123% year-over-year increase in the price of steel mill products in August 2021. Tata Steel predicts steel costs to rise from the decade's average of about $400 per ton to $600 per ton in the next few years.

These material shortages and price escalations raise concerns for construction firms about their financial viability. Input costs have surged more rapidly than the average bid prices for projects. In December 2021, the average input cost rose nearly 20%, while the average bid price only increased by 12.5%. A recent Deloitte survey reveals that 20% of engineering and construction respondents anticipate worsening their operating profitability and industry margins.

Virtual Construction Is Rapidly Evolving. The construction industry uses many new technologies, especially those related to virtual design and visualization. These technologies, like Building Information Modeling (BIM) and Construction Management Software, help plan and manage construction projects.

Virtual design and construction (VDC) involves creating and visualizing structures in a virtual environment before building them in the real world. You can access these virtual environments on your computer or mobile devices or through augmented and virtual reality.

This trend is gaining popularity because fixing mistakes in construction is pretty costly—around 30% of total construction expenses. Virtual design reduces this by allowing builders to simulate and plan structures in a virtual space before construction begins. Building Information Modeling (BIM) is widely used among VDC tools, enabling architects, engineers, and others to create virtual models of physical buildings or structures.

As of 2023, the BIM (Building Information Modeling) market is valued at around $8.1 billion. Although the construction industry faced challenges during the pandemic, It's anticipated to recover in this decade.

North America is predicted to lead the market in the next few years, capturing over 30%. BIM technology has seen an adoption rate of 60-70%, although it took about 35 years to gain widespread use. However, there's progress, with a 2020 report revealing that 73% of respondents used BIM compared to 2011 when almost half had never heard of it.

BIM, along with modular construction and prefabrication, is helping construction firms stick to budgets and tight schedules. Construction Management Software (CMS) is now crucial for major construction companies. The global CMS industry is valued at $9.3 billion and is expected to reach $23.9 billion by 2031.

Construction projects involve multiple parties and various simultaneous tasks. CMS supports construction managers by centralizing data, blueprints, and documents in one accessible location.

3D Printing Is Gaining Ground. The construction 3D printing market is experiencing remarkable growth, with a projected Compound Annual Growth Rate (CAGR) of 100.7% through 2030. This advanced form of 3D printing can utilize diverse materials such as concrete, geopolymers, fiber, sand, and even biodegradable options like mud, soil, and straw in the construction of houses.

While traditional 3D printing in construction was limited to the frame and walls, rapid technological advancements now enable the integration of plumbing and electrical fixtures into buildings through 3D printing.

The construction industry benefits significantly from 3D printing, particularly in terms of time and cost savings. Based in California, Mighty Buildings constructed a 700-square-foot 3D prefabricated home, the Mighty Duo B, in just eight weeks, costing $314 per square foot. The company reports a 75% reduction in construction timelines for its projects.

A notable advantage of 3D printing in construction is lower costs, requiring fewer workforce hours and reduced labor costs. A commercial building in Dubai was constructed with 50% less labor than a typical one. Black Buffalo 3D, a provider of large-scale 3D construction printers, claims a 40% cost reduction compared to traditional on-site wooden frames. ICON, a company using 3D printing for home construction, built a 650-square-foot home in 24 hours at a cost of $10,000.

Given the cost-saving potential of 3D printing in construction, organizations like Habitat for Humanity are closely monitoring this emerging trend.

Construction Automation. Early adopters of automation in the construction industry are achieving significant goals such as reduced waste, improved safety, enhanced productivity, and closing the workforce gap by incorporating robotics and automation strategies. The market for construction robots is projected to reach $359 million by 2031.

A survey commissioned by ABB last year revealed that over half of construction companies are currently using robots, and 81% anticipate introducing robots within the next decade. These robots are employed for various on-site and off-site tasks, with one notable example being the TyBOT—a rebar-tying device. TyBOT, which ties rebar at a rate of 1,100 intersections per hour, provides a 40% boost in productivity compared to human labor and reduces worksite injuries. TyBOT's creator, Advanced Construction Robotics, plans to release IronBot in 2022, capable of self-placing up to 5,000-pound bundles of rebar, potentially improving productivity by at least 250% when used alongside TyBOT.

Dusty Robotics is another company that is achieving success with construction automation. Its FieldPrinter autonomously marks layouts on concrete slabs, offering a process up to 10 times faster than traditional human methods. Fully integrating with CAD and BIM models, this automated solution requires only one operator and a tablet interface.

The market for autonomous construction vehicles is even more significant, valued at $11.86 billion in 2022, with an expected growth of nearly 18.5% through 2026. Built Robotics, founded in 2016, contributes to this sector by developing software and hardware to automate construction equipment. Its Exosystem, installed on late-model excavators and backhoes, operates within a geofenced area, monitored by a 360-degree camera. Although the Exosystem has essentially replaced the operator that generally would be piloting the excavator or backhoe, the Exosystem is so precise in its earth moving and excavating capabilities; this will open the door for future technology professionals to maintain, monitor and program these types of advanced technology within the construction industry.

So, what do all of these changes within the construction industry mean for you as an estimator?

It's hard to know what will come about with all of the rapidly advancing technology in construction. What isn't hard to understand is this: As the industry changes, you will need to change your methods as an estimator.

Unfortunately, this technology will take time for an estimator to understand how to estimate using this technology effectively. From what we've read in this chapter, these technologies are being tested and used on a very small scale. At some point, you will attempt to calculate the costs for technologies like these in your estimate. Still, you'll likely lack the historical data from previous estimates and previously completed projects to validate your calculations.

As a construction estimator, you must always remain open to the newest construction advancements and stay fluid in your estimating capabilities to embrace these new technologies in creating your estimates.

9

RESOURCES FOR THE CONSTRUCTION ESTIMATOR

THROUGHOUT YOUR CAREER as a construction estimator, you will need a keen understanding of cost estimation within many aspects of construction projects. As you've read in "Construction Project Estimating 101," we've broken down many estimating fundamentals to foster the growth of both new estimators and seasoned professionals, and these fundamentals are yours to build upon. You can decide how they fit into your methods and processes and utilize them in your daily workflow. We've talked quite a bit about efficiency in estimating and how efficiencies can speed up the estimating process, allowing you to create more estimates in a shortened period – ultimately leading to more bidding opportunities won.

This chapter covers a few crucial aspects, such as exploring advanced estimation courses and certifications, online takeoff services, and construction estimation programs.

As we start this chapter, the goal is to educate you as the estimator about the available learning resources and many of the digital tools available for construction estimators. Whether you're seeking to enhance your skills, discover innovative online tools, or optimize your estimating processes through cutting-edge programs, this chapter should provide an excellent baseline for you to build upon.

ADVANCED ESTIMATING COURSES AND CERTIFICATIONS

Just as with any career choice outside of the construction industry, career advancement is a positive career move, even if it's only for personal satisfaction.

There are numerous opportunities in the construction world to gain an 'edge' over others performing your same job function. Although typically, in the United States, estimating certifications are not required to become an estimator, there is no downside to accumulating certifications that prove you've had education beyond fieldwork.

This is especially true if the certifications you seek or classes you take are related to construction estimating or any of the topics covered in this book. As a construction estimator, you have many opportunities to advance your career into differing realms of the industry.

I've listed some of the most recognizable online education purveyors that offer classes to enhance an estimator's education.

> **Coursera**. Coursera is an online platform that revolutionizes education by offering courses, specializations, and degrees from top universities and organizations worldwide. Launched in 2012, Coursera provides a flexible and accessible learning experience, enabling individuals to acquire new skills, enhance existing ones, and earn recognized credentials.
>
> Coursera operates on a user-friendly model that allows learners to access high-quality education at their own pace. Users can browse through a diverse catalog of courses covering various subjects. Once a course is selected, learners engage in video lectures, interactive quizzes, and peer-graded assignments. Coursera's platform fosters a

collaborative learning environment where participants can connect with instructors and peers through discussion forums.

Moreover, Coursera offers specializations, which are curated sequences of courses focusing on a specific skill set or topic. Users can also pursue complete degree programs online, providing a flexible alternative to traditional education. Coursera offers online courses you can complete on your timeline and at your own pace.

Coursera has teamed with Columbia University in New York to provide construction-related courses categorized as 'Construction Management Specialization.' The specific estimating-related course is listed below.

Construction Cost Estimating and Cost Control — *In this course, grasp the essential principles of cost estimation, focusing on the fundamentals and intricacies of the design phase for practical cost assessment. Learn the intricacies of concluding a project during the close-out period. Explore elements such as punch lists, final approval processes, and the turnover to the client, ensuring a comprehensive understanding of project completion—master cost control methodologies with a specific emphasis on the Earned Value Method. Understand how to implement and leverage this method to ensure efficient and effective control over project expenses.*

For more information on related courses in the Construction Management Specialization tract, visit coursera.org.

Estimating Academy. The American Society of Professional Engineers offers Estimating Academy, an online education path that caters to new estimators, field workers looking to transition to the business side of construction, and seasoned estimators.

The Estimating Academy offers individual course selections and a full course tract that will earn the student a certificate in construction estimating. ASPE's complete course certificate program is explained similarly to this: *ASPE's exclusive Certificate in Construction Estimating consists of six essential courses tailored to equip novice estimators with core competencies and fundamental skills. This program offers a thorough initiation into foundational principles, covering plan reading, estimating math, bidding practices, materials and processes, and the art of preparing an estimate. Whether you're entering the estimating domain for the first time, seeking a refresher, or aiming to provide training for your staff, ASPE's Certificate in Construction Estimating stands as the contemporary solution for accessible online estimating education.*

The six-course ASPE Estimating Academy certificate program is comprised of these courses: Basic Estimating Math, Plan Reading for Estimating, Introduction to Construction Estimating I, Introduction to Construction Estimating II, Estimating and Bidding, Construction Materials and Processes I.

If an estimator wishes to take any of Estimating Academy's single courses, information can be found at aspenational.org/page/CiCE.

RSMeans Data from Gordian. In the construction sector, RSMeans data is synonymous with comprehensive cost details, a reputation held for decades. Robert Snow Means, a Civil Engineer, meticulously documented construction costs in leather-bound books crafted at his kitchen table. By the early 1940s, his peers were so impressed by his detailed tracking of equipment, material, and labor costs that they began expressing interest in purchasing his homemade "cost books."

Presently, RSMeans data is provided by Gordian. The database encompasses over 92,000 line items, with cost engineers dedicating over 30,000 hours annually to research and validate the costs. While the cost information is still available in printed books, it is also accessible through CDs and dynamic estimating software.

Gordian is the foremost global provider of facility and construction cost data, software, and services spanning every stage of the building lifecycle. As a trailblazer in Job Order Contracting (JOC), Gordian offers its exclusive RSMeans data and provides facility intelligence solutions. Gordian's solutions empower clients to enhance efficiency, achieve optimal cost savings, and elevate building quality by covering the entire spectrum from planning to design, procurement, construction, and operations.

RSMeans Data from Gordian offers multiple online classes to students who wish to enhance their estimating capabilities across various sectors. The most valuable course for a construction estimator is the *Fundamentals of Construction Cost Estimating Self-Paced Training Course.*

The course is described as follows: *The emphasis is on unit price estimating for facility renovation, repair, and remodeling. By integrating hands-on skill development with discussions on best estimating practices and real-life challenges, this insightful online course is designed to enhance your estimating skills. It will keep you updated with crucial concepts and offer valuable tips and guidelines. This knowledge can save you time and assist in avoiding costly oversights and errors in your estimating processes.*

For more information regarding this course from RSMeans Data from Gordian or their related courses, point your browser to rsmeans.com.

Each of these three companies providing online, go-at-your-own-pace courses is a viable solution if you want to gain further insights as a construction estimator beyond what we've discussed in this book.

Next, we will look at certification programs for estimators.

ESTIMATING CERTIFICATIONS

Construction cost estimation is pivotal in the construction industry, playing a crucial part in the success of a project. It involves predicting the costs of a construction endeavor, encompassing raw materials, labor, and timelines. Inaccurate estimations can result in budget overruns and missed deadlines, underscoring the importance of skilled and precise estimators.

This emphasis on precision is where a construction estimating certification becomes paramount. These certifications offer a clear advantage, demonstrating the holder's expertise and commitment to this essential task. They offer training that enhances the capacity to provide accurate estimates, ultimately reducing expensive errors and improving overall project efficiency.

We will examine six essential certifications in the field of construction estimating: the Professional Certificate in Construction Estimating (PCSE), Procore Estimator Certification (PEC), Certified Professional Estimator (CPE), Certified Cost Estimator/Analyst (CCE/A), Certified Cost Professional (CCP), and Construction Cost Estimating and Cost Control (CCECC) certification. Each of these certifications provides distinct advantages for aspiring and experienced construction estimators, paving the way for career success in construction estimating.

Procore Estimator Certification (PEC). The Procore Estimator Certification (PEC) is a specialized certification that centers around the Procore software, a widely utilized construction management platform. This certification offers comprehensive training on Procore estimating modules and other associated applications.

Earning the PEC comes with distinct advantages. First, it demonstrates proficiency in utilizing Procore software—a valuable skill given the widespread use of the software in the construction industry. Secondly, it opens up opportunities for companies that currently use or plan to implement Procore for their estimating and other project management needs. Lastly, obtaining a PEC sets the stage for continuous learning and adaptability in the rapidly evolving technological landscape of the construction sector.

Professional Certificate in Construction Estimating (PCSE). The Professional Certificate in Construction Estimating (PCSE) offers a comprehensive certification program that delves deeply into the intricacies of construction estimating. Participants gain valuable insights into various estimating techniques, strategies, tendering, procurement, project cost control, and estimating construction materials and methods.

The benefits of PCSE are multifaceted. First, it equips participants with the skills to accurately estimate project costs, mitigating the risk of budget overruns. Secondly, it enhances employment prospects by demonstrating a solid foundational understanding of the construction industry and its practices. Lastly, the certification provides a platform for participants to connect and network with a community of like-minded professionals, fostering opportunities for potential job placements and partnerships in the industry.

Certified Professional Estimator (CPE). The Certified Professional Estimator (CPE) is a distinguished certification provided by the American Society of Professional Estimators (ASPE). This certification imparts in-depth knowledge of various types of estimates, from conceptual to definitive. It emphasizes the importance of maintaining a professional standard of practice and ethical behavior in estimating.

Obtaining the CPE certification comes with several notable benefits. First, the certification is widely recognized globally, broadening the horizons for international job opportunities. Secondly, it is a testament to one's commitment to high ethical standards in estimating and fostering trust and reliability with employers and clients. Lastly, the CPE certification creates avenues for career advancement, thanks to the program's comprehensive knowledge requirements that enhance the skills and expertise of certified professionals.

Certified Cost Professional (CCP). The Certified Cost Professional (CCP) certification, administered by AACE International, validates an individual's proficiency and knowledge in cost management, encompassing areas such as estimating, project controls, and economic analysis.

The significance and benefits associated with obtaining the CCP certification are noteworthy. First, it equips professionals with a profound understanding of cost management, empowering them to manage and control project costs effectively. Secondly, the certification opens doors to enhanced opportunities in project planning and cost control roles, acknowledging the specialized skills acquired through the certification process. Lastly, achieving the CCP certification contributes to establishing a professional's reputation for competence and skill in the field of cost management, adding a valuable credential to their professional profile.

Certified Cost Estimator/Analyst (CCE/A). The Certified Cost Estimator/Analyst (CCE/A) is a globally acknowledged certification conferred by the International Cost Estimating and Analysis Association (ICEAA). This certification uniquely combines cost estimating and analysis into a unified program, offering participants a more holistic understanding of the entire construction project lifecycle.

Pursuing the CCE/A certification is motivated by several compelling reasons. It fosters the development of expertise in both cost estimation and analysis, contributing to a comprehensive grasp of effective cost management practices. Additionally, the certification broadens the perspective on project management by encompassing aspects such as cost prediction, cost tracking, and risk assessment. Also, individuals holding the CCE/A certification become more appealing to employers seeking professionals handling various cost-related aspects throughout a project.

Construction Cost Estimating and Cost Control (CCECC). The Construction Cost Estimating and Cost Control (CCECC) certification, available through esteemed educational institutions such as Columbia University, focuses on equipping individuals with expertise in cost control strategies for construction projects. This certification program provides practical skills and knowledge to ensure that project costs remain within the designated budgets.

Gaining the CCECC certification comes with distinct advantages. First, it imparts valuable skills in controlling and reducing costs in construction projects, a pivotal competency essential for the success of any project. Second, individuals with this certification find opportunities in project management and financial control roles, where the ability to contain costs is a central responsibility. Additionally, obtaining the CCECC certification provides a competitive edge by showcasing practical, project-ready skills to employers, enhancing the professional appeal of certified individuals in the construction industry.

Here is a simplified recap of the certifications you've read about above.

The PCSE provides a comprehensive foundational understanding of the industry and its practices, positioning it as an excellent choice for beginners. On the other hand, the PEC is tailored for individuals seeking to showcase their proficiency in Procore software.

The CPE stands out as a globally recognized and reputable certification, offering extensive knowledge on different types of estimates.

Opting for the CCE/A certification ensures a holistic understanding of cost estimation and analysis, appealing to those desiring comprehensive knowledge in cost management.

The CCP concentrates on honing cost management skills, potentially leading to project planning and cost control roles.

Last, the CCECC imparts practical skills in cost control, making it an ideal choice for those specializing in this aspect.

Each certification presents unique benefits and learning opportunities. The key lies in aligning your individual career goals, expertise level, and the commitment you are willing to make regarding time and cost. You can select the construction estimating certification that best suits your aspirations and needs that align with your career goals.

OUTSOURCING ACCURATE TAKEOFFS

There is an option that many estimators prefer to use when faced with a takeoff of any size. There are multiple viable options for third-party takeoff services. These services require you to email them the project plans and specifications, and they will perform your takeoff.

Why use a third-party takeoff service? Using third-party takeoff companies to execute construction takeoffs plausibly is a strategic approach. By outsourcing this task, estimators can redirect their focus to other critical tasks, optimizing efficiency. The primary advantage of third-party takeoff services lies in their consistency in the estimation process. Leveraging paid services ensures a commitment to accuracy above industry standards, making it a valuable investment for construction estimators.

Takeoff Monkey. Takeoff Monkey is a professional construction service that empowers contractors of all sizes. Their goal is to improve the quality and quantity of your bids significantly. Beyond mere quantities, their deliverables are enriched with thorough notes. Takeoff Monkey meticulously identifies discrepancies and contradictions within the documents, provides valuable cost-saving ideas and detailed references, and addresses any elements an estimator seeks.

Integra Global Solutions. Delivering top-notch construction plan quantity takeoff services, Integra Global Solutions caters to contractors, sub-contractors, and suppliers globally, spanning the US, Canada, UK, and Australia. Their professional takeoff team specializes in diverse commercial and residential projects, ensuring you receive a meticulous list of materials complete with quantities and precise measurements.

Upon receipt of a finalized takeoff, they provide a comprehensive materials overview and highlight any plan discrepancies or assumptions made due to missing information. Committed to expediency, their team prioritizes promptly delivering the most accurate construction plan quantity takeoff services, enhancing your bidding success.

Precise Estimate Inc. (PEI). Precise Estimate Inc. stands behind its reputation as the epitome of reliability in project estimation. Their commitment to delivering swift and efficient services sets a high bar, catering to valued customers across residential, commercial, and industrial domains, making PEI unparalleled in the market. What distinguishes PEI is its unrivaled expertise in estimation services, serving many satisfied clients. They're proud to offer the most effective estimation pricing, characterized by minimal variances, a testament to the profound expertise derived from their human and capital resources.

Using a third-party takeoff service may seem to be a luxury for some estimators, and that ties back to the workflow word we've discussed throughout this book. Companies typically prefer to use in-house estimators for their projects, as let's face it — subcontracting out the takeoff portion of the estimating process is likely not all that cost-effective. Each third-party takeoff created for an estimate adds cost to the estimate, which may affect the bottom line of the estimate.

ESTIMATING TAKEOFF SOFTWARE

We've talked in depth throughout the book about the availability of online software-based estimating programs. These programs create efficiency, accuracy, and consistency in your estimating methods and processes, ultimately positively affecting your workflow. Below are some of the most used digital estimating programs that are cloud-based or localized to your network.

Buildxact. Buildxact is a comprehensive construction estimating and project management software for small builders, remodelers, and contractors. Its specialty is simplifying complex construction processes, offering an easy-to-use platform that combines features such as on-screen takeoff, estimating, quoting, and project management. The software allows users to track quotes efficiently through a user-friendly dashboard, facilitating faster bidding to win more construction projects.

Buildxact stands out for its powerful construction management capabilities, providing a seamless experience for users engaged in residential, commercial, and industrial projects. With an emphasis on simplicity and effectiveness, Buildxact streamlines the estimating process, making it a valuable tool for professionals in the construction industry.

BuilderTrend Estimating. BuilderTrend Estimating is a leading construction project management software tailored for home builders, remodelers, and contractors. This software specializes in streamlining the estimating process, offering digital tools for precise material and cost estimates. One notable feature is the on-screen takeoff functionality, allowing users to digitize the measuring process and facilitating project planning and estimating.

BuilderTrend's internal data suggests using their takeoff software is 33% faster than manual measuring. With a focus on accuracy, efficiency, and project management, BuilderTrend Estimating stands out as a comprehensive solution for construction professionals, providing a digital roadmap to effectively predict costs, quantities, and project timelines.

HeavyBid by HCSS. HeavyBid by HCSS is a comprehensive construction estimating software designed to streamline the bidding and estimation process for contractors. Specializing in heavy civil construction, HeavyBid allows users to input bid items and quantity information generated from external takeoff programs.

It accurately produces cost estimates by leveraging historical data, verifying material and labor prices, and automating routine tasks. HeavyBid focuses on delivering precise and efficient estimating solutions, enabling contractors to manage complex bidding processes, enhance project efficiency, and make informed decisions.

Houzz Pro. Houzz Pro is a construction estimating software that provides a streamlined and efficient solution for performing takeoffs and creating precise estimates. The software is designed to expedite the estimation process by allowing users to complete takeoffs up to 10 times faster through its intuitive digital takeoff tools. Focusing on convenience, Houzz Pro enables users to measure and markup plans directly on-screen, eliminating the need for printing plans.

This cloud-based construction estimating software facilitates the quick and accurate measurement of plans, aiding estimating professionals in producing detailed estimates rapidly. Whether uploading plans or inputting measurements, Houzz Pro's on-screen takeoff capabilities contribute to its core strength of helping builders and contractors bid more jobs effectively.

Knowify. Knowify is a comprehensive construction management software designed to streamline the operations of contractors and specialty businesses. This software combines CRM, project management, and invoicing functionalities, providing an all-in-one solution for construction professionals. Knowify facilitates efficient project data management, allowing users to run their contracting businesses confidently.

Knowify integrates features like integrated takeoff and estimating, enabling users to handle tasks such as budgeting, managing, and invoicing seamlessly. Home builders, remodelers, and specialty contractors trust it.

PlanSwift. PlanSwift is a leading construction estimating software designed to streamline the takeoff process for contractors and construction professionals. Specializing in accurate and efficient estimations, PlanSwift offers on-screen takeoff capabilities, allowing users to perform measurements and calculations directly on digital blueprints. This feature significantly enhances speed and precision in estimating, ultimately saving time and increasing accuracy.

The software's versatility suits various construction specialties, providing a comprehensive tool for estimating, takeoff, and project cost management.

Procore Estimating. Procore Estimating is a robust construction estimating software designed to enhance project success by facilitating efficient quantity takeoffs, precise estimates, and professional proposals. Specializing in streamlining the estimating process, Procore offers features for general contractors and specialty contractors alike. The software seamlessly integrates takeoff data into the estimating workflow, ensuring accuracy and ease of use.

With capabilities to streamline bidding processes, Procore Estimating aims to optimize project management for construction professionals. While the provided information doesn't explicitly mention on-screen takeoff, Procore is recognized for its comprehensive suite of tools, making it a valuable solution for estimating in the construction industry.

QuoteSoft. QuoteSoft is a comprehensive construction estimating software for HVAC, ductwork, plumbing, and piping contractors. The software offers powerful tools for estimating labor hours and material costs, streamlining the estimation process. With specialized features like on-screen takeoff capabilities, QuoteSoft allows users to import electronic drawings for paper-free takeoffs, enhancing accuracy and efficiency.

QuoteSoft caters to the unique needs of contractors in the construction industry, providing a cloud-based solution for quick bid estimating and on-screen takeoff. QuoteSoft's ability to show labor and material details during takeoff, spool pipe lengths automatically, and display hangers contribute to its effectiveness in optimizing the estimation workflow.

RSMeans Data. RSMeans Data is a renowned construction cost estimating software that simplifies the estimation process for construction projects. Specializing in accurate construction cost estimates, RSMeans Data ensures projects stay within budget and are completed on time. The software provides access to a comprehensive database of construction costs in North America, offering detailed breakdowns of material, labor, and equipment expenses.

With cloud-based functionality, RSMeans Data Online allows users to quickly add, edit, and share price proposals, enhancing the efficiency of estimating tasks. While it may not explicitly mention on-screen takeoff features, RSMeans Data is well-regarded for its ability to provide accurate unit prices and a detailed breakdown of construction costs, making it a valuable tool for professionals in the construction industry.

Sage Estimating. Sage Estimating is a comprehensive construction estimating software designed to streamline the estimation process for commercial and residential contractors across various trades. This software offers tools for estimating, managing bids, and providing project visibility. With a focus on material and labor analysis, Sage Estimating provides a detailed level of estimation, leveraging libraries that come with the software or can be customized.

Integrating On-Screen Takeoff (OST) with Sage Estimating enhances its capabilities, allowing users to incorporate takeoff conditions generated in On-Screen Takeoff with its items and assemblies. This integration facilitates a seamless workflow, enabling users to perform quantity takeoffs efficiently. Sage Estimating caters to the diverse needs of construction professionals, offering multiple takeoff methods and ensuring accuracy in estimating construction costs.

Stack Estimating. Stack Estimating is a cloud-based construction estimating software that offers a comprehensive solution for professional contractors across various trades and business sizes. This powerful software facilitates the estimation process, from takeoffs to proposal generation, enabling users to work faster and with unmatched accuracy. The specialty of Stack Estimating lies in its ability to empower estimators to win more profitable work by providing a user-friendly platform for performing fast and accurate takeoffs.

It is designed to streamline the bidding process, allowing contractors to bid more efficiently in less time. With features for measurements, tracking, and organized calculations, Stack Estimating is a versatile tool that caters to the needs of construction professionals, making it an invaluable asset for those seeking precision and efficiency in their estimating endeavors.

Trimble Autobid. Trimble Autobid is a comprehensive mechanical estimating software designed for MEP (Mechanical, Electrical, Plumbing) contractors specializing in commercial mechanical, piping, and plumbing projects. The software streamlines the estimation process, offering total customization to meet the specific needs of mechanical contractors. It covers various stages of the construction process, providing 3D design software, estimating tools, and more.

Trimble Autobid Mechanical stands out for its ability to deliver accurate project cost estimates, facilitating faster and more efficient bidding processes. The software's features enable MEP contractors to create simplified takeoffs, define precise project costs, and enhance overall project management. With its focus on customization and accuracy, Trimble Autobid is a valuable tool for mechanical contractors seeking optimal efficiency in estimating and bidding for diverse construction projects.

As you've read in this chapter about topics like furthering your education as an estimator, challenging yourself to earn a certificate that will bolster your professional career in construction estimating, or being intrigued by the thought of using a subcontracted takeoff service or a computerized estimating takeoff program, keep it in mind that all of the options on this chapter are extremely useful as an estimator.

You may want to put earning a certificate in estimating on your long-term radar, or you may want to start researching online takeoff programs to familiarize yourself with a program that will fit your workflow and create efficiency in your daily duties as an estimator.

As this chapter ends, remember this — construction estimating is not learned overnight. As an estimator, you will constantly learn, refine, and understand the best process.

FINAL THOUGHTS

We have covered an enormous amount of information in this book, and I hope you feel better positioned to enter into the construction estimating field with new or additional knowledge. Additionally, I hope you better understand the importance of the job, the steps you'll take to revise or refine your methods and processes, and the ability to create a workflow for yourself that brings efficiency, consistency, and accurate estimates every time.

The information I provided in the book was learned through many years of trial and error in my construction estimator and project manager processes. Understandably, some of the book's elements might be crossover information for estimators or project managers. Still, it's excellent information to have either way, as an estimator is often the project manager.

We've learned in the book that having a solid fundamental baseline is the key to starting your estimating career off on the right foot. Understanding the importance of having accurate and consistent estimates every time is imperative to fostering consistency throughout your career.

In my career, I've done enough estimates that I don't need to recall from memory what steps A, B, and C are — they just come naturally, like riding a bike (think back to the bike analogy we went over earlier in the book). I start my estimating process the same way each time, and this is how I know I haven't skipped or overlooked any steps.

We've discussed the challenges and pitfalls an estimator can encounter by not having a proper workflow for their estimating process. If your workflow is seamless, it only enhances your ability to stay consistent. If a thought pops into your mind like "Did I do this step?" or "What's next for this estimate?" your workflow may need to be examined, and a slight change may be in order.

A great workflow will reduce the time it takes to perform takeoffs, gather material and subcontractor quotes, and put the final estimate together before presenting the estimate or submitting it on bid day.

I've given you as much information as possible about why you should consider using technology for estimating. The estimating software programs available are very technologically advanced and considerably reduce the time the estimator takes to perform a takeoff by hand.

If you are using or already use computerized estimating software, just for fun, create a little experiment for yourself. Before a future estimate of the mid-range size, perform the takeoff for your estimate using the computer-based software, and then do a takeoff by hand — and time yourself for each of your takeoffs. You'll be amazed at the difference in hours or minutes you save using a digital takeoff program.

Once you figure out the difference in hours or minutes, multiply this number by 20 (representing your following 20 estimates), and then divide that number by 60 (minutes in an hour). The resulting number is the extra time you can't get back by performing takeoffs by hand. It's a bit daunting how inefficient performing takeoffs by hand are.

I want to go back in time and speak to career construction estimators from decades ago and tell them what the future looks like and how technological advancements have streamlined our positions as estimators. I bet they would scoff at the thought of technology and make some choice comments like "Back in the day" or "You have it so easy." They're right. Regarding software—based estimating—we have it easy, but we also have it consistent. And that's the goal.

We've done a deep dive into understanding project specifications and the need to thoroughly understand the scope of every project we work on. If we don't understand exactly what we are estimating, we might as well roll up the plans and do something else for the day. Upfront knowledge of every project is imperative to the bottom line.

As an estimator, I've seen projects that contractors have ultimately had to write checks for at project closeout because one or two minor details were missed in the estimate. Still, those one or two minor details were worth one or two more zeros on that project's profit and loss wrap-up sheets. Estimating errors usually comes with a dollar value that rectifies them; as estimators, it's our job to protect those dollars.

We observed some similarities and differences when estimating in different sectors like residential and commercial, and we've also broken down why communication and collaboration are necessary for an estimator. If people aren't talking or sharing information, there's likely no chance that the estimate will win the bid for the project, as the final number will not be accurate. Each team member on the bidding team needs to do their part, communicate effectively, and contribute to the overall goal of winning the bid.

You've learned about some of the often-missed elements of an estimate, like insurance, legal requirements, labor interruptions, and ethical estimating practices. These are all essential elements of an estimate, and time should be allocated to each estimate to create accurate associated costs for these elements and more.

As an estimator, quite possibly in your career, you'll be able to get within 5 - 10% of the projected hours to complete that project you've estimated and won, which in my book is a win as you clearly understand the need for accuracy and protecting the projected profits on the job. What you may have forgotten, however, may have been a scenario where certain costs delegated to the contractor to provide were spelled out in the job scope or job specifications, and by accident, you may not have read that specification section as you thought it didn't apply to your scope of work. The project wraps up, your portion of the project seems to have made a small profit, and then your company gets notified that a check for a certain amount will be expected to cover the delegated costs in the project specifications. Now, your project is underwater.

That scenario above has never happened to me, but it is a true story. A former colleague found himself in this position on a project he estimated and ran as the project manager when I was very new to estimating. It was perfect for me to get a front-row seat to this error that the estimator made — as it showed me early on in my career that 'picking and choosing' which project specifications I think I need to read was not an option. He unfortunately found out that job specifications aren't optional to read, and that error came with a monetary cost.

We've also discussed how using available technology as an estimator helps refine your workflow, consistency, and accuracy — it's just intelligent estimating practice. In full transparency, I'm a bit 'old school' in doing some things and very technologically savvy in how I do other things regarding estimating.

I have somewhere between 8 - 10 years left of my career, and I have a decade and a half of my methods, processes, and workflow behind me that consistently work for me in my daily duties. If someone were to ask me if it took my whole estimating career to refine those into a system that works for me, I quickly would answer "yes."

Estimating is what I said early on in this book, and that is just what the word means — estimating (not exacting). We aim to get as close as possible to the actual costs factored into each estimate we produce and to put money in the bank after the project ends.

I've been asked many times throughout my career by people curious about estimating the ratio of my projects won versus lost. I started tracking these numbers early in my estimating career, and I can still confidently say that 1 in 10 estimates will end up with a contract for a project.

That number may seem low to you, and here's why. I live in a major metropolitan city in the Midwest. We are in a cold winter climate where many projects are affected by the unforeseen conditions we've talked about in this book. In my early years of estimating, I spent most of my time estimating municipal and airport projects, as the company I worked for had their 'foot in the door,' so to speak, for those types of projects.

I tracked these win/loss numbers, and the projects won revenue numbers for nearly eight years. I did this so I'd have the historical data I needed for projects of similar nature and size, but maybe in a different market or another part of the city. Having this historical data of my efforts was vital for future projects similar to projects I had already estimated or run, and my goal was always to perform better using this data.

I knew the market in which I was estimating. I knew the contractors I was bidding against and the general contractors I was bidding to. I worked with this group of general contractors regularly (not all the time), so they knew my communication and collaboration style, and they knew that the projects I estimated and managed would be clean — meaning there wouldn't be too many instances that I'd have to communicate about ill-regarded elements of a project or an estimate.

On projects I didn't win, I would call the contractors I submitted bids to and ask to be provided with the winning bid number, in addition to the losing bid numbers of my competition. I did this so I would have historical data. From those numbers, I could extrapolate where my estimate might have been high or even where my estimate might have fallen short.

Without having data to learn from as an estimator, it's almost like you're playing a game of Darts every time you create an estimate. We aim at the bullseye on the dartboard every time, but each time we throw a dart, we're six inches either way off of that bullseye or off the board entirely.

Construction estimating is a data-driven career. Additionally, just as a hedge fund manager has to know their business inside and out to provide their clients with a return on their investment, construction estimators must have knowledge beyond counting items they see on a blueprint to be effective.

As estimators, we create the bottom line number and win job contracts. That's the simplest way to explain what we do. Just exactly how we do our job is what you've nearly completed reading. Many cogs are turning in different directions when you're in an estimating career. You'll need to identify and define those cogs, and you'll need to work to keep those cogs turning throughout your career.

You'll find great success in your career as an estimator if you are in the mindset and the workflow to continually improve through refining and revising your methods and processes.

Thank you for reading 'Construction Project Estimating 101'. Your support of this book means more to me than I can express.

I wish you well in your career as an estimator in this fast-paced world of construction, and as I learned to say very early on when I found out I didn't win a project that I created the estimate for — "On to the next one."

With humble gratitude,

P.D. Mason

(P.S. — don't forget to check out the invaluable Glossary that starts on the next page!)

Help Another Construction Estimating Professional!

There's an exciting time ahead of you in your career, and you're just at the start of it. You have the ability to help another construction estimator *discover their full potential* after reading this book!

By sharing your honest opinion of this book and a little about what you found inside, you'll help construction estimators discover the basic foundational guidance they might not have found otherwise.

It only takes a minute or two at most to leave your thoughts — and those thoughts are incredibly valuable to others searching for construction estimating books.

Your Honest Amazon book review can have the potential to help thousands develop their career!

Thank you so much for your support. Your review is incredibly vital, and I appreciate your *HONEST* Amazon review tremendously.

Scan the QR code to leave your review on Amazon.

GLOSSARY

A

American Institute of Architects (AIA). AIA is the most prominent design organization in the world, working to transform the practice of architecture. It aims for a zero-carbon, resilient, and sustainable approach to architecture and construction. The AIA provides standardized forms and documents widely used in the construction industry, including those related to billing and payments. One notable document is the AIA G702 Application and Certificate for Payment.

As-Built Drawings. As-built drawings represent the final set of drawings produced during or after construction. They document the actual conditions, dimensions, and locations of elements as constructed, serving as a reference for future modifications or maintenance.

B

Backcharge. Backcharge refers to charging costs back to a subcontractor or supplier due to errors, omissions, or deficiencies in their work, typically deducted from the amount owed.

Bid Bond. A Bid Bond is a surety bond submitted with a bid to guarantee that the bidder if awarded the contract, will enter into a contract and provide the required performance and payment bonds.

Bid Form. The Bid Form is a document used in the bidding process that outlines the essential terms of the contractor's offer, including the bid price, completion time, and other relevant details.

Bid Peddling. Bid Peddling involves an unethical practice where a subcontractor approaches a contractor after bid submission, offering to lower their bid to secure the subcontract.

Bid Price. The bid Price is the total amount of money a contractor proposes to charge for completing a construction project as specified in the bidding documents.

Bid Shopping. Bid Shopping occurs when a general contractor reveals subcontractor bids to competitors or attempts to get lower bids from subcontractors after being awarded the contract, leading to unfair competition and potential legal issues.

Bid Tabulation. A document summarizing the bids received for a construction project, detailing the bid amounts from various contractors. It aids in selecting the winning bid by comparing and analyzing the proposals.

Bill of Quantities. A detailed list specifying the quantities and types of materials, labor, and services required for a construction project. It forms the basis for cost estimation and project planning.

Blueprint. A technical drawing or plan that provides detailed specifications of a construction project. It includes architectural, structural, electrical, and plumbing details.

C

Change Directive. An official order in construction projects, issued by the owner or architect, directs changes to the contract. It is used for urgent changes before a formal Change Order is processed.

Change Order. A written order signed by the owner or owner's agent authorizing changes in the construction work, including modifications to the project's scope, schedule, or cost.

Change Order Proposal. A document submitted by a contractor to propose changes to the original construction contract. It outlines the modifications and associated costs.

Competitive Bid. The process of soliciting bids from multiple contractors for a construction project. Contractors submit competitive proposals, and the lowest responsive bidder is typically awarded the contract.

Constructability. The assessment of how well a project can be constructed, considering factors such as feasibility, cost, and ease of construction. It aims to optimize the construction process.

Constructive Acceleration. It occurs when a contractor is forced to accelerate work to meet a project deadline due to delays caused by the owner or other factors. The contractor may be entitled to compensation for the additional costs incurred.

Constructive Change. A change to the construction contract that is not explicitly stated but is implied through the actions or conduct of the parties involved. It may entitle the contractor to compensation.

Contingency. Contingency refers to an allowance of funds set aside in a project budget to cover unforeseen events or circumstances that may arise during the construction process. It acts as a buffer to handle unexpected expenses or changes in project scope.

Contingent Fee. A contingent fee in construction typically refers to a fee dependent on certain conditions being met. For example, a contractor may receive a fee based on the successful completion of a project or achieving specific performance milestones.

Contractor's Qualification Statement (CQS). The Contractor's Qualification Statement is a document submitted by a contractor during bidding. It provides information about the contractor's qualifications, experience, financial stability, and other relevant details to demonstrate their capability to undertake the construction project.

Cost Breakdown. A cost breakdown is a detailed itemization of all the costs associated with a construction project. It typically includes labor, materials, equipment, overhead, and other expenses, providing a transparent breakdown of the total project cost.

Cost Code. A cost code is a system of identifying and categorizing different types of costs within a construction project. It helps track and manage expenses for specific activities, allowing for better cost control and analysis.

Cost Engineering. Cost engineering involves the application of engineering principles and techniques to estimate, control, and analyze project costs. It includes cost estimating, cost control, and value engineering to optimize project costs.

Cost Estimate. A cost estimate approximates the total cost of a construction project. It is based on available budgeting, bidding, and overall project planning information.

Cost Estimating Manual. A cost-estimating manual is a document or set of guidelines that provides standardized procedures and methodologies for estimating construction costs. It helps ensure consistency and accuracy in the estimation process.

Cost Index. A cost index is a numerical value representing relative cost changes over time for a specific set of goods or services. In construction, it is often used to adjust historical cost data to account for inflation or changes in market conditions.

Cost of Construction Index. The Cost of Construction Index is a specific cost index that reflects the changes in construction costs over time. It is used to adjust project budgets or estimates to account for variations in labor, materials, and other construction-related expenses.

Cost Reimbursement. Cost reimbursement is a contract in construction where the contractor is reimbursed for their allowable costs and sometimes paid an additional fee. This type of contract is often used when the scope of work is uncertain or highly complex.

Cost-Plus Fee. The cost-plus fee is a compensation structure in construction contracts where the contractor is reimbursed for allowable costs and is paid an additional fixed fee or percentage of costs as profit.

Cost-Plus Fixed Fee (CPFF). Cost-plus fixed fee is a type of cost-plus fee contract where the contractor is reimbursed for allowable costs, and a predetermined fixed fee is added to cover profit.

Cost-Plus Incentive Fee (CPIF). A cost-plus incentive fee is a type of cost-plus fee contract that includes a base fee along with an additional incentive fee. The incentive fee is tied to the contractor's performance against specified performance criteria, encouraging cost savings and efficiency.

Cost-Plus Percentage of Cost (CPPC). Cost-plus percentage of cost is a compensation structure in construction contracts where the contractor is reimbursed for allowable expenses, and the fee is calculated as a percentage of the total costs. This can lead to an increase in the fee as costs escalate.

Cradle-to-Grave. Cradle-to-grave refers to the entire lifecycle of a construction project, from its inception or planning phase (the "cradle") to its completion or decommissioning (the "grave"). It encompasses all stages, including design, construction, and maintenance.

Critical Path. The critical path in construction is the sequence of activities that determines the overall duration of a project. It represents the longest path from the project's start to finish and identifies tasks that must be completed on time to avoid delaying the entire project.

D

Deductive Change. A deductive change in construction refers to a change order that reduces the contract price. It may involve the removal of specific work or a decrease in the scope of the project, leading to a lower overall cost.

Defective Bid. A defective bid in construction occurs when a bid submitted by a contractor contains errors, omissions, or inaccuracies that may affect the bid's validity or the contractor's ability to fulfill the contract requirements.

Deliverables. In construction, deliverables are the tangible outcomes or results produced or completed during a project. They can be specific items, documents, or milestones expected to be delivered to the client, stakeholders, or project team within predefined timeframes.

Depreciation. Depreciation in construction refers to the reduction in the value of assets over time due to wear and tear, obsolescence, or other factors. It is an accounting method used to allocate the cost of an asset over its useful life.

Design Development. Design development is a phase in the design process of a construction project where the initial concept design is refined and developed further. It involves detailed planning, coordination, and decision-making to create a comprehensive and executable design.

Design Fee. The design fee is the compensation paid to design professionals, such as architects or engineers, for their services in creating the design and plans for a construction project. It is a contractual fee agreed upon between the client and the design team.

Design-Assist. The design fee is the compensation paid to design professionals, such as architects or engineers, for their services in creating the design and plans for a construction project. It is a contractual fee agreed upon between the client and the design team.

Design-Bid-Build. Design-Bid-Build is a traditional project delivery method in construction where the design phase is completed before contractors bid on the project. Once the design is finalized, it is put out for competitive bidding, and the construction contract is awarded to the lowest qualified bidder.

Design-Build. Design-Build is a project delivery method where a single entity, the design-build team, is responsible for the project's design and construction. This integrated approach aims to streamline communication, reduce risks, and enhance project efficiency.

Design-Build-Operate (DBO). Design-Build-Operate is an extended version of the design-build model, where the entity not only designs and constructs the project but also operates and maintains it for a specified period. This model is often used in infrastructure projects such as water treatment plants.

Design-Construct. Design-Construct is another term for the Design-Build project delivery method, emphasizing the integrated nature of a single entity's design and construction processes.

Direct Costs. Direct costs in construction are expenses that can be directly attributed to a specific project. These include costs for materials, labor, equipment, and other resources directly associated with the construction work.

Due Diligence. Due diligence in construction refers to the comprehensive research and investigation conducted by project stakeholders to assess the feasibility, risks, and potential issues associated with a construction project before committing to it.

E

Earned Value. Earned value is a project management technique in construction that measures work progress by assigning a value to completed tasks. It helps assess the project's planned performance versus actual progress and cost.

Earned Value Management. Earned Value Management (EVM) is a project management technique in construction that integrates cost, schedule, and scope to assess project performance. It involves measuring the work performed against the planned value to evaluate the project's progress and efficiency.

Earnest Money. In the context of construction contracts, Earnest money is a monetary deposit made by a bidder as a show of good faith and commitment to the bidding process. It is typically submitted with a bid to demonstrate the bidder's serious intent to fulfill the contract if awarded.

Escalation Clause. An escalation clause in a construction contract allows for adjustments to the contract price based on specified conditions, such as changes in labor costs, material costs, or other economic factors. It helps address the impact of inflation or unforeseen cost increases.

Escrow. Escrow in construction refers to a financial arrangement where a neutral third party holds funds or documents until specific conditions are met. It is often used in earnest money transactions, performance bonds, or other contractual obligations.

Estimating Accuracy. Estimating accuracy in construction refers to the degree of precision and reliability in the estimation of project costs. Accurate estimating is crucial for budgeting and project planning, and it involves considering various factors that may influence costs.

Estimating Period. The estimating period in construction is the timeframe during which cost estimates are prepared for a project. It typically occurs during the early stages of project planning and design when detailed information about the scope and requirements is gathered.

Estimating Software. Estimating software in construction refers to computer programs and tools designed to assist in accurately and efficiently estimating project costs. These software applications often include features for cost modeling, database management, and project analysis.

Estimating Team. The estimating team in construction is a group of professionals responsible for preparing cost estimates for a project. This team may include cost estimators, quantity surveyors, and other experts collaborating to provide accurate and comprehensive estimates.

F

Fast-Track Construction. Fast-track construction is an approach that compresses the project schedule by overlapping design and construction phases. It allows construction to begin before the entire design is complete, enabling earlier project completion but requiring careful coordination.

Feasibility Study. A feasibility study in construction is a comprehensive analysis conducted to assess a proposed project's practicality, viability, and potential success. It examines technical, economic, legal, and operational aspects to determine whether the project is feasible and advisable.

Field Engineer. A field engineer in construction is a professional responsible for on-site management and coordination of engineering activities. They ensure construction plans are implemented correctly, resolve technical issues, and oversee the day-to-day construction operations.

Field Order. A written directive or instruction issued by the project owner or architect to the contractor during the construction phase. Field orders typically address changes, clarifications, or additional work not covered by the original contract documents.

Field Overhead. Field overhead in construction refers to the indirect costs associated with on-site construction activities. These costs include site supervision, temporary facilities, equipment, and other expenses specific to the construction site.

Financial Closeout. Financial closeout in construction marks the completion of a project's financial transactions. It involves settling all outstanding financial matters, finalizing payments, and completing financial documentation related to the project.

Fixed Fee. A fixed fee in construction is a predetermined, non-adjustable amount agreed upon in a contract. It is paid to the contractor as compensation for their services, regardless of the costs incurred during the project.

Flowchart Estimate. A flowchart estimate in construction is a visual representation that illustrates the sequence of activities, resources, and decisions involved in the estimating process. It helps in understanding and improving the efficiency of the estimation workflow.

Force Account. Force account in construction refers to a payment method where the actual costs of labor, materials, and equipment are reimbursed, often with an additional fee. This method is used when the scope of work is difficult to define in advance.

Force Account Work. Force account work in construction involves executing work on a time and materials basis. It is often used when unforeseen conditions or project scope changes make establishing a fixed price impractical.

Force Majeure. Force majeure in construction refers to unforeseeable and unavoidable events or circumstances that prevent one or both parties in a contract from fulfilling their obligations. These events, such as natural disasters or political upheavals, are typically beyond the parties' control.

G

General Conditions. General conditions in construction refer to the standard provisions and requirements in a construction contract that set the overall terms, responsibilities, and procedures for the project. They cover items such as project administration, permits, and safety.

General Requirements. General requirements in construction are specific project requirements that are not related to the physical construction work but are essential for project execution. These may include permits, insurance, bonds, and other administrative aspects necessary for project compliance.

Grant. In construction, a grant typically refers to financial assistance from a government entity or organization for a specific construction project. Grants may be awarded for various purposes, such as infrastructure development or community improvement.

Guaranteed Maximum Price (GMP). Guaranteed Maximum Price (GMP) is a contract type in construction where the contractor agrees to complete the project for a specified maximum cost. The contractor is responsible for covering the additional expenses if the actual costs exceed the agreed-upon GMP.

Guaranteed Maximum Price (GMP) Proposal. A GMP proposal in construction is a document submitted by a contractor that outlines the maximum price at which they commit to completing a project. It includes a breakdown of costs and is used during the negotiation phase of a GMP contract.

H

Home Office Overhead. Home office overhead in construction refers to the indirect costs incurred by a contractor's central office that are not directly attributable to a specific project. These costs may include administrative expenses, salaries of home office staff, and general company overhead.

I

Implied Warranty. An implied warranty in construction refers to an unwritten guarantee that certain aspects of the construction work will meet standard expectations, even if not explicitly stated in the contract. It is a legal concept that assumes certain warranties exist by default.

In-House Estimator. An in-house estimator in construction is an individual employed by a construction company responsible for preparing cost estimates for the company's projects. This contrasts with hiring external or freelance estimators.

In-Place Cost. In-place cost in construction refers to the cost associated with the actual installation or construction of a component or system. It includes labor, materials, and overhead directly related to the work being performed.

Incentive Contract. An incentive contract in construction is a contractual arrangement that provides financial incentives to the contractor for achieving specific performance objectives, such as completing the project ahead of schedule or under budget.

Indemnity. Indemnity in construction is a contractual provision where one party agrees to compensate the other for losses, damages, or liabilities incurred during the project. It serves as a means of financial protection against specified risks or claims.

Independent Cost Estimate. An assessment of the anticipated cost of a construction project conducted by a third party, separate from the contractor or project team. It provides an unbiased estimate to help in budgeting and decision-making.

Indirect Costs. Costs that are not directly attributed to a specific construction project but are necessary for the overall operation of the construction company. These may include overhead expenses like administrative salaries, utilities, and office supplies.

Indirect Expense. Like indirect costs, indirect expenses are those incurred in a construction business's general operation that cannot be directly linked to a specific project.

Insurance. A risk management tool that provides financial protection against potential losses or damages during construction projects. Types of insurance commonly used in construction include liability insurance, property insurance, and workers' compensation.

Insurance Certificate. A document issued by an insurance company that provides evidence of insurance coverage. It outlines the type and amount of insurance the contractor holds, ensuring the necessary coverage is in place.

Integrity. In the context of construction, integrity refers to the quality of being honest and having strong moral principles. It is crucial in maintaining trust and reliability within the construction industry.

Invitation to Bid (ITB). A formal document issued by a project owner to solicit bids from qualified contractors for a construction project. The ITB outlines project details, specifications, and the bidding process.

J

Job Order Contracting (JOC). A construction procurement method where contractors are pre-selected to perform various construction projects based on pre-negotiated unit prices. JOC is often used for repetitive, smaller-scale projects.

JOC Program. A program that implements Job Order Contracting involves establishing contracts with pre-selected contractors for a range of construction projects over a specified period.

L

Labor Agreement. A formal agreement between a construction employer and a labor union representing workers. It outlines terms and conditions of employment, including wages, working hours, benefits, and dispute resolution mechanisms.

Labor Burden. The total indirect costs associated with employing a construction worker, beyond the direct wages. This includes items such as taxes, insurance, benefits, and other expenses related to labor.

Labor Productivity. A measure of the efficiency and output of labor in a construction project. It assesses the work accomplished per labor unit, often expressed as work units per labor hour.

Labor Rate. The amount paid per hour or unit of work to a construction worker. It includes both the worker's wages and any additional labor burden costs.

Land Development Cost. The total cost of preparing raw land for construction includes expenses such as grading, utility connections, site preparation, and infrastructure development.

Last Planner System. A production planning and control system used in construction management to improve workflow and project reliability. It involves collaboration among project teams to create a more realistic and achievable construction schedule.

Lead Time. The amount of time required for ordering, receiving, and preparing materials or equipment before they are needed in the construction project. Lead time is crucial for project planning to ensure timely availability of resources.

Lean Construction. A construction management approach that focuses on maximizing value and minimizing waste throughout the construction process. It aims to improve efficiency, reduce costs, and enhance project delivery.

Letter of Intent (LOI). A written document expressing an individual or organization's intention to enter into a formal agreement or contract in the future. In construction, an LOI may precede the formal contract negotiations.

Liability. Legal responsibility or obligation for any potential harm, damage, or loss. In construction, liability may refer to the responsibility of parties involved for accidents, defects, or other issues that may arise during the project.

Lien Waiver. A document signed by a contractor or subcontractor, relinquishing their right to file a mechanics' lien on a property. It is often exchanged for payment and indicates that the party has been paid and waives their right to place a lien on the property for the specific work done.

Life Cycle Cost. The total cost of owning, operating, maintaining, and disposing of a construction project or facility over its entire life cycle. It includes initial construction costs as well as costs incurred during the operational phase.

Life Cycle Costing. The process of evaluating and analyzing the total costs associated with a construction project or asset throughout its life cycle. This includes considering costs beyond the initial construction phase, such as maintenance and operating expenses.

Line Item Estimate. An itemized estimate where the costs for each component or line item of a construction project are listed separately. It provides a detailed breakdown of the expenses for transparency and accuracy.

Liquidated Damages. A predetermined amount of money agreed upon in a contract that a party must pay if they fail to fulfill specific contractual obligations, such as completing the construction project within the agreed-upon timeframe.

Liquidation. The process of converting assets into cash. In construction, liquidation may refer to the sale of surplus materials or equipment to recover funds or the dissolution of a company's assets.

Load Factor. Load factor in construction refers to the calculation that determines the proportion of common or shared spaces in a commercial property, allocating costs to tenants based on their use of these areas.

Loaded Labor Rate. The total cost per hour for a construction worker, including both direct labor costs (wages) and indirect costs (such as benefits, taxes, and overhead).

Low Bid Method. A procurement method in which the contract is awarded to the contractor submitting the lowest bid. This method is standard in competitive bidding for construction projects.

Low Bidder. The contractor or construction company that submits the lowest bid in a competitive bidding process. The low bidder is typically awarded the construction contract.

Lump Sum. A fixed and agreed-upon total contract price for all the work in a construction project. In a lump sum contract, the contractor is responsible for completing the project for the specified amount, regardless of actual costs incurred.

M

Mark-to-Market. A financial accounting method used to reevaluate the fair market value of assets or liabilities regularly. In construction, it may be applied to assess the current market value of properties or projects.

Markup. An additional amount or percentage added to the cost of materials, labor, and other expenses to determine the total contract price. It represents the contractor's profit and overhead costs.

Material Escalation. An increase in the cost of construction materials over time, often due to factors such as inflation, supply chain disruptions, or changes in market conditions.

Material Overhead. The indirect costs associated with handling and processing construction materials that are beyond the actual cost of the materials themselves. It includes expenses like storage, transportation, and handling.

Material Takeoff. The process of determining the quantities and types of materials required for a construction project based on project drawings and specifications. It is a crucial step in estimating and procurement.

Mechanic's Lien. A legal claim placed on a property by a contractor, subcontractor, or supplier who has not been paid for work or materials provided. The lien provides a security interest in the property until the debt is satisfied.

Milestone. A significant event or stage in a construction project noting the completion of a specific phase or the achievement of a critical objective. Milestones are often used to track progress and manage project timelines.

Mobilization. Preparing and moving construction equipment, personnel, and resources to a project site at the start of the construction project. Mobilization costs are often included in the project budget.

Modular Construction. A construction method where building components or modules are prefabricated off-site and assembled on-site. This approach can save time and costs compared to traditional on-site construction.

Multi-Prime Contract. A construction project delivery method where different aspects or phases of the project are awarded to multiple prime contractors, each responsible for a specific scope of work. This can allow for more specialized expertise and coordination.

Multiple-Baseline Schedule. A project scheduling technique involves creating and managing multiple project baselines for different project scenarios or changes. It allows for better tracking and management of project changes.

N

Negligence. The failure to exercise reasonable care or the breach of duty, resulting in harm or damage. In construction, negligence may refer to actions or omissions that lead to accidents, defects, or other issues.

Negotiated Contract. A construction contract that is not awarded through a competitive bidding process. Instead, the terms and conditions are negotiated between the owner and the contractor, allowing for more flexibility in contract terms.

No-Damage-for-Delay Clause. A contractual provision that limits or eliminates the contractor's liability for damages resulting from project delays, even if factors beyond the contractor's control cause the delay.

Notice to Proceed (NTP). A formal written notification from the project owner to the contractor authorizing the start of construction work. The NTP indicates the official commencement date for the project.

O

On-Site. Refers to activities, personnel, or items at the physical construction site. It includes the actual project location where construction work is being carried out.

Open Bid. A procurement process in which contractors submit bids for a construction project in response to an open invitation. The bid process is competitive, and the contract is typically awarded to the lowest qualified bidder.

Open Book. A construction contract arrangement where the owner has access to the contractor's financial records, allowing for transparency in costs, profits, and other financial aspects of the project.

Oral Bid. A bid presented verbally by a contractor during a bidding process. While less common and often not recommended due to the lack of documentation, oral bids may be accepted in certain circumstances.

Overhead. Indirect costs incurred by a construction company that is not directly tied to a specific project but contributes to the overall operation of the business. Overhead costs may include administrative expenses, utilities, rent, and other general costs.

Overlaying. A term used when placing a revised set of blueprint drawings over an original drawing. Typically, to identify the differences in construction drawings. Often used in electronic estimating programs.

Owner. The individual or entity that owns the construction project and has the authority to make decisions regarding the project. The owner may be a private individual, a corporation, or a government entity.

Owner's Contingency. A reserve fund set aside by the owner to cover unforeseen or unexpected costs that may arise during the construction project. It serves as a buffer against uncertainties and changes in project scope.

Owner's Representative. A person or entity appointed by the owner to act on their behalf in managing and overseeing the construction project. The owner's representative ensures that the project is executed according to the owner's requirements and interests.

P

Panda System. A construction scheduling method that involves overlapping or compressing project phases to expedite project completion. It aims to reduce the overall project duration by allowing certain activities to proceed concurrently.

Pay When Paid. A payment clause in a construction contract stipulates that the subcontractor will be paid only when the contractor receives payment from the project owner. It links subcontractor payments to the contractor's receipt of funds.

Payment Bond. A surety bond provided by the contractor to the project owner as a guarantee that subcontractors, suppliers, and laborers will be paid for their work and materials. It protects against non-payment issues.

Payroll Burden. The additional costs associated with employing construction workers beyond their wages. Payroll burden includes expenses such as taxes, insurance, and benefits.

Peer Review. An evaluation process where construction industry professionals review and assess a project's plans, designs, or specifications to ensure quality, accuracy, and compliance with industry standards.

Performance Bond. A surety bond provided by the contractor to the project owner to guarantee that the contractor will perform the work according to the terms and conditions of the contract. It protects the owner in case of non-performance by the contractor.

Performance Specification. A detailed description in a construction contract that outlines the specific performance requirements and standards that a completed project must meet. Unlike design specifications, performance specifications focus on the intended outcome rather than specifying how the work should be done.

Permit. Official authorization or approval granted by a government or regulatory body, allowing the commencement of construction or certain activities. Permits ensure that the construction project complies with local building codes and regulations.

Permitting Process. The series of steps and approvals required from relevant authorities to obtain the necessary permits for a construction project. The permitting process ensures that the project adheres to zoning laws, building codes, and other regulations.

Pert Chart. Program Evaluation and Review Technique (PERT) Chart is a visual representation of a project schedule that illustrates the sequence of activities, their dependencies, and the critical path. It helps in project planning and management.

Pilot Study. A small-scale preliminary study conducted to test the feasibility, time, cost, risk, and performance of a particular aspect of a construction project before implementing it on a larger scale.

Plumbing Estimating. The process of calculating the estimated costs associated with plumbing work in a construction project. This includes the cost of materials, labor, overhead, and other relevant expenses.

Portfolio Management. The strategic management of a collection of construction projects or assets as a portfolio. It involves balancing and optimizing resources, risks, and returns across multiple projects to achieve overall organizational objectives.

Pre-Bid Conference. A meeting held before the bidding process where representatives from the owner and potential bidders discuss project details, specifications, and answer questions. It provides clarification and ensures a common understanding among bidders.

Pre-Bid Estimate. An initial cost estimate prepared by a contractor before submitting a bid for a construction project. It serves as a preliminary assessment of the costs involved in completing the project.

Pre-Bid Meeting. Another term for a pre-bid conference is a meeting held before the bidding process where project details, specifications, and other relevant information are discussed with potential bidders. It helps ensure clarity and transparency in the bidding process.

Pre-Bid Walkthrough. A site visit conducted by potential bidders before submitting their bids for a construction project. The walkthrough allows contractors to familiarize themselves with the site conditions and gather information necessary for accurate bidding.

Pre-Construction Services. Services provided by a contractor before the actual construction phase begins. This may include project planning, cost estimation, scheduling, value engineering, and other activities to ensure a smooth and efficient construction process.

Pre-Engineered Building. A building structure designed and manufactured off-site in standard sections or components and then assembled on-site. Pre-engineered buildings often use standardized designs for efficiency and cost-effectiveness.

Pre-Engineered Metal Building (PEMB). A type of pre-engineered building made primarily of metal components. PEMBs are designed for quick and efficient assembly and are often used for industrial, commercial, or storage purposes.

Pre-Engineered Steel Building. Like a pre-engineered metal building (PEMB), a pre-engineered steel building is specifically constructed using steel components. These buildings are known for their strength, durability, and versatility.

Pre-Engineered Structure. A pre-designed and fabricated off-site construction structure or system, with standardized components assembled on-site. Pre-engineered structures can include buildings, bridges, and other types of infrastructure.

Pre-Existing Conditions. The conditions or circumstances that exist at a construction site before the commencement of a new project. It is essential to assess and account for pre-existing conditions during project planning and design.

Pre-Qualification. The process by which potential bidders or contractors are evaluated and assessed for their qualifications, experience, financial stability, and other criteria before being allowed to bid on a construction project.

Pre-Qualification Statement. A document submitted by a contractor or vendor during the pre-qualification process. It includes information about the company's qualifications, experience, financial standing, and other relevant details.

Pre-Qualified Bidder. A contractor or bidder who has completed the pre-qualification process and is deemed qualified to participate in the bidding for a construction project. Pre-qualified bidders have met specific criteria set by the project owner or manager.

Preliminary Estimate. An initial or early-stage estimate of the costs associated with a construction project. Preliminary estimates are made before detailed project plans, and specifications are available and serve as an early indication of potential project costs.

Prevailing Wage. The hourly wage, benefits, and overtime rates established by the government are the minimum compensation for workers on public construction projects. Prevailing wage rates aim to ensure fair compensation for labor.

Prime Contractor. The primary contractor responsible for overseeing and managing the entire construction project. The prime contractor may subcontract certain portions of the work but retains overall responsibility for project delivery.

Profit and Loss Statement. A financial statement that summarizes the revenues, costs, and expenses incurred by a construction company during a specific period. It provides an overview of the company's financial performance, including profit or loss.

Profit Margin. The percentage difference between the total revenue earned and the costs incurred by a construction project or company. Profit margin is a key indicator of financial performance and efficiency.

Progress Payment. Payment made to a contractor at specific stages or milestones of a construction project is usually based on completing a predetermined percentage of the work. Progress payments help contractors cover ongoing costs during the project.

Project Closeout. The final phase of a construction project is when all contractual obligations are fulfilled, and the project is officially completed. It involves final inspections, documentation, and the handover of deliverables to the owner.

Project Executive. A high-level management position overseeing multiple construction projects within a company or organization. The project executive ensures that projects align with organizational goals and objectives.

Project Labor Agreement (PLA). A pre-hire agreement between project owners, contractors, and labor unions that establishes the terms and conditions for employment on a construction project. PLAs often outline wages, benefits, and work conditions.

Project Management Software. Software designed to assist in planning, scheduling, tracking, and managing construction projects. Project management software often includes features for collaboration, document management, scheduling, and cost tracking.

Project Manager. An individual responsible for planning, coordinating, and overseeing all aspects of a construction project. The project manager ensures that the project is completed on time, within budget, and meets the specified quality standards.

Project Milestone. A significant point or event in a construction project that marks the completion of a specific phase or achievement of a critical objective. Milestones are used to track progress and manage project timelines.

Project Owner. The individual, organization, or entity that owns or initiates a construction project. The project owner is ultimately responsible for the project's success and may act as the client or end-user of the completed facility.

Project Scope. The detailed description of the work to be performed in a construction project includes the objectives, deliverables, specifications, and other relevant details. The project scope outlines what is included and excluded from the project.

Proposal. A document submitted by a contractor or service provider in response to a request for proposal (RFP). The proposal outlines the contractor's approach, qualifications, and cost estimates for the construction project.

Proposal Form. A standardized document or template contractors use to submit their proposals in a consistent format. The proposal form typically includes sections for project details, cost breakdowns, and contractual terms.

Public Bid. The process of inviting bids from multiple contractors or vendors for a construction project that is publicly funded or commissioned by a government agency. Public bids are typically subject to competitive bidding laws and regulations.

Punch List. A list of items, tasks, or issues must be addressed or completed before a construction project can be considered fully finished or accepted. The punch list is typically created during the final inspection phase.

Q

Quality Assurance. The systematic process ensures that a construction project meets specified quality standards and requirements. Quality assurance involves implementing processes and controls to prevent defects and maintain high-quality outcomes.

Quality Control (QC). The process of inspecting, testing, and monitoring construction activities and materials to verify that they meet the specified quality standards. Quality control is essential to ensuring a construction project's overall quality.

Quality Management Plan. A document outlining the processes, procedures, and standards that a construction project will follow to ensure the delivery of a high-quality end product. The quality management plan includes measures for quality control and assurance.

Quantity In Place. The actual amount or quantity of construction materials or work installed or completed at a specific time during a construction project. It is a measure of progress.

Quantity Survey. The process of estimating and measuring the quantities of materials and work required for a construction project. Quantity surveying is essential for cost estimation and project planning.

Quantity Surveyor. A professional specializing in quantity surveying is responsible for estimating, measuring, and managing the quantities of materials and work involved in a construction project. Quantity surveyors play a crucial role in cost management.

Quotation. A formal statement or document a contractor or supplier provides to a potential client detailing the costs, terms, and conditions for providing goods or services. It is a preliminary offer before a formal contract is established.

Quotation Price. The specified price or cost is mentioned in a quotation provided by a contractor or supplier. It represents the amount the client is expected to pay for the goods or services outlined in the quote.

Quotation Request. A formal document or communication from a potential client requesting quotations or bids from contractors or suppliers for specific goods or services. It includes details about the project or requirements.

Quotation Worksheet. A document contractors or suppliers use to organize and calculate the costs associated with providing goods or services. The quotation worksheet helps in preparing accurate and detailed quotations.

Quote. A brief statement or estimate of the costs, terms, and conditions for providing goods or services. A quote is typically less formal than a formal proposal or contract and may be provided in response to a customer's inquiry.

Quote Form. A standardized document or template contractors or suppliers use to provide quotes in a consistent format. The quote form typically includes itemized costs, terms, and contact information sections.

Quoted Price. The specific monetary amount provided in response to a request for a quote. The quoted price represents the cost that a contractor or supplier is offering for goods or services.

Quoted Rate. The specified cost per unit, hour, or other defined measure is mentioned in a quotation. Quoted rates are often used for labor or services provided by contractors.

Quoted Specification. A detailed description of the materials, standards, and work specifications is provided in a quotation. Quoted specifications outline the characteristics and requirements for the construction project.

Quoted Time. The estimated duration or time frame mentioned in a quotation for completing a specific construction project or task. Quoted time provides the client with an expectation of the project timeline.

Quoted Unit. The specific measurement or unit used to quantify the goods or services provided in a quotation. Quoted units can include square footage, linear feet, or other relevant measures.

Quoted Value. The total estimated worth or value of the goods or services outlined in a quotation. The quoted value is calculated based on the quoted price and the quantity or volume of the items specified.

Quoted Work. The scope of work or services is detailed in a quotation. Quoted work outlines the specific tasks, activities, and deliverables the contractor or supplier offers.

Quoting. Preparing and submitting quotations in response to requests from potential clients. Quoting involves estimating costs, specifying terms, and providing details about the goods or services offered.

Quoting Accuracy. The degree of precision and correctness in estimating costs, timelines, and specifications provided in a quotation. Quoting accuracy is essential for establishing trust and avoiding misunderstandings with clients.

Quoting Process. The systematic series of steps and activities contractors or suppliers undertake to prepare and submit quotations. The quoting process includes gathering information, estimating costs, and presenting a formal offer to potential clients.

Quoting Software. Computer programs or applications designed to assist contractors or suppliers in preparing and managing quotations. Quoting software streamlines the process, helping with cost estimation, proposal creation, and tracking.

Quoting System. A comprehensive set of processes, tools, and software contractors or suppliers use to manage the entire quotation process. A quoting system typically includes components for estimating, pricing, and creating formal quotes.

Quoting Tool. A specific software feature or application designed to aid in creating and managing quotations. Quoting tools may include features for cost estimation, itemized pricing, and customization of quotes.

Quoting Workflow. The sequence of steps and processes involved in preparing and submitting quotations. Quoting workflows may vary among construction companies but generally include gathering information, estimating costs, and creating formal quotes.

Quoting Worksheet. A document or spreadsheet contractors or suppliers use to organize and calculate the costs associated with providing goods or services. The quoting worksheet aids in the detailed breakdown of the expenses for accurate quotations.

Quoting Worksheet Template. A pre-designed format or layout that serves as a starting point for creating quoting worksheets. Templates provide a standardized structure for organizing and presenting information in a quotation.

Quoting Your Work. The process of presenting and pricing the work or services you provide in a quotation. Quoting your work involves communicating the value and cost of your offerings to potential clients.

Quoting Your Worth. The practice of assigning a fair and appropriate value to your work or services when preparing a quotation. Quoting your worth involves considering expertise, quality, and market standards.

Quoting Zone. A phase or area within the quotation process where contractors or suppliers focus on creating and finalizing quotes. The quoting zone involves cost estimation, pricing, and proposal preparation.

R

Re-Bid. The process of inviting new bids or quotations for a construction project that has undergone changes or modifications. Re-bidding may occur due to changes in project scope, budget adjustments, or other factors that necessitate a new round of competitive bidding.

Reconciliation. The process of comparing and aligning financial records or accounts to ensure accuracy and consistency. In construction, reconciliation may involve reconciling project costs, payments, or other financial data.

Reimbursable Costs. Costs incurred by a contractor during a construction project that the project owner can reimburse. Reimbursable costs are typically outlined in the contract and may include items such as materials, equipment, or additional labor.

Request for Information (RFI). A formal document issued by a party involved in a construction project to request clarification or additional information about project details, specifications, or other relevant matters. RFIs are used to resolve uncertainties during the project.

Request for Proposal (RFP). A document issued by a project owner or client to solicit proposals from contractors or service providers for a construction project. The RFP outlines project details, requirements, and evaluation criteria.

Request for Quote (RFQ). A document used to invite contractors or suppliers to submit quotations for specific goods or services. An RFQ typically includes required product or service details and solicits pricing information.

S

Schedule of Values. A detailed breakdown of the costs associated with different components or phases of a construction project. The schedule of values is used for progress billing and provides a transparent view of project costs.

Schematic Design. The initial phase in the design process of a construction project is where rough sketches or diagrams are created to explore and communicate design ideas. Schematic design helps in defining the project's overall concept.

Scale Rule. A measuring tool, often in the form of a ruler, is designed to facilitate measuring distances on construction drawings or plans. Scale rules are calibrated to represent a specific ratio or scale.

Scope Creep. The gradual expansion or addition of tasks, features, or requirements beyond the initially defined scope of a construction project. Scope creep can lead to increased costs and delays if not properly managed.

Site Analysis. The process of evaluating and studying a construction site's characteristics, conditions, and constraints. Site analysis includes assessments of topography, soil conditions, environmental factors, and other site-specific considerations.

Specifications. Detailed written or graphic instructions, requirements, and standards define construction project materials, workmanship, and performance criteria. Specifications provide essential details for contractors to follow during project execution.

Subcontractor. A company or individual hired by the principal or prime contractor to perform a specific portion of the work on a construction project. Subcontractors are typically specialists in their field and contribute to the overall project.

Subcontractor Default Insurance (SDI). Insurance coverage protects a project owner or general contractor if a subcontractor defaults on their contractual obligations. SDI provides financial protection against the risks associated with subcontractor non-performance.

Submittal. The process of submitting documents, shop drawings, samples, or other materials to the project owner or design team for review and approval. Submittals ensure that the work complies with project requirements.

Substantial Completion. The stage in a construction project is when the work is deemed complete or nearly complete, allowing the owner to occupy or utilize the facility for its intended purpose. Substantial completion is a significant project milestone.

Surety Bond. A surety or bonding company provides a financial guarantee to ensure that a contractor fulfills its contractual obligations. Surety bonds may include bid bonds, performance bonds, and payment bonds.

T

Takeoff. The process of quantifying and estimating the quantities of materials required for a construction project based on project drawings and specifications. Takeoff is an essential step in cost estimation.

Tenant Improvement (TI). Tenant improvement refers to the customization or alterations made to leased commercial or residential space to meet the specific needs and preferences of the tenant.

U

Unit Cost. The cost per unit of a specific quantity or measurement, such as cost per square foot or cost per linear foot. Unit costs are used in estimating and budgeting for construction projects.

Unit Price. The price per unit of measurement for a specific item or service provided in a construction contract. Unit prices are used for items that may vary in quantity during the project.

V

Value Analysis. A systematic process of evaluating and analyzing the functions of a construction project to identify opportunities for improving performance, reducing costs, or enhancing value. Value analysis seeks to optimize project outcomes while controlling costs.

Value Engineering. A systematic and organized approach to improving the value of a construction project by assessing its functions and components. Value engineering aims to optimize performance, quality, and cost-effectiveness.

Value Management. An inclusive term encompassing various techniques and methods, including value engineering, used to maximize value in construction projects. Value management involves strategic decision-making to achieve project objectives efficiently.

Variance. The difference between the planned or budgeted amount and the actual amount or performance. In construction, variance analysis helps assess deviations from the original plan regarding cost, schedule, or other project parameters.

W

Wage and Hour Laws. Legal regulations governing the working hours, wages, and conditions of employment for construction workers. Wage and hour laws ensure fair compensation and working conditions in the construction industry.

Warranty. A written guarantee or assurance a contractor or manufacturer provides regarding the quality, performance, and durability of materials, workmanship, or completed construction work. Warranties typically specify the duration and terms of coverage.

Working Drawings. Detailed and precise drawings, plans, and diagrams that provide specific instructions for the construction or execution of a project. Working drawings serve as a guide for contractors during the construction phase.

Z

Zone Pricing. A pricing strategy in construction where costs are assigned or adjusted based on geographic zones or regions. Labor rates, material costs, or market conditions in specific areas may influence zone pricing.

Zoning. The process of dividing land into zones or districts with specific regulations and restrictions on how the land can be used. Zoning regulations control the type of construction, land use, and density in different areas within a jurisdiction.

REFERENCES

101 INTRODUCTION TO CONSTRUCTION ESTIMATING, ENGR 034 CLASS SYLLABUS - CEI. (2022, October 18). CEI. https://constructionclasses.com/101-introduction-to-construction-estimating/

2024 engineering and construction industry outlook. (2023, November 5). Deloitte Insights; Deloitte. https://www2.deloitte.com/us/en/insights/industry/engineering-and-construction/engineering-and-construction-industry-outlook.html

Accelerate the Estimating Workflow for Building Construction | Togal.ai. (2023). Togal.ai. https://www.togal.ai/blog/accelerate-the-estimating-workflow-for-building-construction

Alger, M. (2023, August 15). *How to estimate remodeling jobs: An accurate pricing guide.* Buildertrend. https://buildertrend.com/blog/estimate-remodeling-jobs/

Andrew. (2023, November 21). *Why Collaboration is the Crucial Factor in Takeoff and Estimating.* Kreo.net; Kreo Sodtware. https://www.kreo.net/news-2d-takeoff/why-collaboration-is-the-crucial-factor-in-takeoff-and-estimating#:~:text=By%20in-volving%20all%20stakeholders%2C%20leveraging,builds%20trust%20a-mong%20project%20teams

APX Construction Group. (2024, January 10). APX Construction Group. https://apxconstructiongroup.com/how-to-calculate-commercial-construction-cost-per-square-foot-in-2022/

Average home price per square foot U.S. 2000-2022 | Statista. (2022). Statista; Statista. https://www.statista.com/statistics/682549/average-price-per-square-foot-in-new-single-family-houses-usa/

Barrett, K. (2022, May 20). *Construction Cost Estimating: What Is It & How Do You Calculate It.* Constructconnect.com; ConstructConnect. https://www.constructconnect.com/blog/construction-cost-estimating

Cole, C. (2022, August). *What to know about Buildertrend's takeoff software.* Buildertrend. https://buildertrend.com/blog/buildertrend-takeoff/

Competitive, in. (2023). *Utilities One.* Utilities One. https://utilitiesone.com/best-practices-for-construction-estimation-and-bidding-in-competitive-markets

Construction Cost Estimate: Basics, 3 Methods & Templates. (2021). FreshBooks. https://www.freshbooks.com/hub/estimates/construction-cost-estimate#:~:text=In%20that%20case%2C%20we%20can,bid%20esti-mates%2C%20and%20control%20estimates

Construction Cost Estimating: A Step-By-Step Guide | Procore. (2024, January 12). Procore; Procore. https://www.procore.com/library/construction-estimating

Construction Disputes: How To Resolve Them? | ProEst. (2021, August 19). ProEst. https://proest.com/construction/tips/resolving-disputes/

Construction Estimating Software. (2022). Procore; Procore. https://www.procore.com/estimating

Construction fact sheet: Rebar-tying tools | Centre of Research Expertise for the Prevention of Musculoskeletal Disorders (CRE-MSD). (2023, October 24). Uwaterloo.ca. https://uwaterloo.ca/centre-of-research-expertise-for-the-prevention-of-musculoskeletal-disorders/resources/fact-sheets-and-handouts/construction-fact-sheet-rebar-tying-tools

Construction, Plumbing and HVAC Ductwork Estimating Software. (2023, January 31). QuoteSoft. https://quotesoft.com/

Construction Robots. (2016). Construction Robots. https://www.constructionrobots.com/

Construction, in. (2023a). *Utilities One*. Utilities One. https://utilitiesone.com/ensuring-compliance-with-legal-and-regulatory-requirements-in-construction-estimation-and-bidding

Construction, in. (2023b). *Utilities One*. Utilities One. https://utilitiesone.com/strategies-for-effective-dispute-resolution-in-construction-projects

Ellis, G. (2022, January 6). *Guide to Building Collaboration in Construction - Digital Builder*. Digital Builder. https://constructionblog.autodesk.com/collaboration-construction/

Ellis, G. (2023, March 17). *Guide to Construction Estimating: 4 Winning Tips to Improve*. Digital Builder. https://constructionblog.autodesk.com/construction-estimating/

Estimator, S. (2023a, December 29). *Role of Risk Management in Construction Cost Estimating*. Medium; Medium. https://medium.com/@sydneyestimator.com.au/role-of-risk-management-in-construction-cost-estimating-6c7ebfcd24ac

Estimator, S. (2023b, December 30). *Mastering Residential Construction Estimating: Avoiding Common Pitfalls*. Medium; Medium. https://medium.com/@sydneyestimator.com.au/mastering-residential-construction-estimating-avoiding-common-pitfalls-752bdbd4c012

Find Support Addressing Ethics in Construction Estimating. (2022, December 26). American Institute of Constructors. https://aic-builds.org/find-support-addressing-ethics-in-construction-estimating/

Frank Lloyd Wright Quote. (2024). A-Z Quotes. https://www.azquotes.com/quote/709548

Fundamentals of Construction Cost Estimating Self-Paced Training Course. (2023). Rsmeans.com. https://www.rsmeans.com/products/training/online/introduction-to-construction-cost-estimating-19930

Home Estimating & Construction Management Software. (2023, July 25). Buildxact US. https://www.buildxact.com/us/

How AI Estimating Software Increases Profitability Of Construction Firms With Faster Takeoffs | Togal.ai. (2021). Togal.ai. https://www.togal.ai/blog/ai-estimating-software

How Construction Risk Profiles Affect Cost Estimates. (2021). Hm-Ec.com. https://www.hm-ec.com/blog-posts/how-construction-risk-profiles-affect-cost-estimates-hm

https://www.bobvila.com/authors/Glenda-Taylor. (2022, January 11). *See Inside Habitat for Humanity's First 3D-Printed Home—and the Future of Construction*. Bob Vila. https://www.bobvila.com/articles/habitat-for-humanity-3d-printed-home/

https://www.facebook.com/Treehugger. (2018). *Affordable House Can Be 3D Printed for $4,000 in Less Than 24 Hours*. Treehugger. https://www.treehugger.com/icon-d-printed-affordable-homes-4858287

in. (2022, March 23). *The value of collaboration in your construction project*. Tekla.com. https://www.tekla.com/resources/articles/the-value-of-collaboration-in-your-construction-project

Introduction to estimating. (n.d.). Https://Www.pearson.com/En-Us/Higher-Education.html. Retrieved January 15, 2024, from https://www.pearsonhighered.com/assets/samplechapter/0/1/3/4/013470116X.pdf

Jones, K. (2021, December 9). *5 Benefits of Using Construction Takeoff Software*. Constructconnect.com; ConstructConnect. https://www.constructconnect.com/blog/5-benefits-of-using-construction-takeoff-software

Jones, K. (2022, December). *9 Inspiring Quotes About Construction*. Constructconnect.com; ConstructConnect. https://www.constructconnect.com/blog/9-inspiring-construction-quotes

Knowify - Construction management software - 14-day free trial. (2024, January 3). Knowify. https://www.knowify.com/

Learn how to set the scope for a construction project effectively by following six steps: identify the objectives, define the deliverables, establish the scope statement, create the scope management plan, validate the scope, and control the scope. (2023, July 20). Linkedin.com. https://www.linkedin.com/advice/0/how-do-you-set-scope-construction-project#:~:text=To%20set%20the%20scope%20for%20a%20construction%20project%2C%20define%20objectives,scope%20to%20ensure%20project%20success

Learn some strategies to improve your estimation skills and processes for civil engineering projects, such as scope definition, data verification, risk analysis, and feedback collection. (2023, November 21). Linkedin.com. https://www.linkedin.com/advice/0/what-strategies-can-you-use-ensure-consistent-po0gf

Learn the best practices and standards for preparing and presenting construction estimates, including value engineering and life cycle costing techniques. (2023, May 31). Linkedin.com. https://www.linkedin.com/advice/1/what-best-practices-standards-preparing

lephare. (2022a, June 14). *How to Write a Scope of Work for Construction Projects*. Cedreo; Cedreo. https://cedreo.com/blog/scope-of-work-construction/

lephare. (2022b, August 11). *Residential Construction Costs Estimates: How to Predict Expenses*. Cedreo; Cedreo. https://cedreo.com/blog/residential-construction-cost-estimates/

McKinsey & Company. (2020). *The next normal in construction How disruption is reshaping the world's largest ecosystem*. https://www.mckinsey.com/~/media/McKinsey/Industries/Capital%20Projects%20and%20Infrastructure/Our%20Insights/The%20next%20normal%20in%20construction/The-next-normal-in-construction.pdf

Mitchell, D. (2023, May 11). *How to Beat the Clock in Construction Estimating (Time*

Management). Archdesk; Archdesk. https://archdesk.com/blog/time-management-construction/

Moody, J. (2023, December 28). *The Estimating Edge.* Estimating Edge. https://www.estimatingedge.com/five-tips-to-streamline-the-construction-estimating-process/

Mortlock, M. (2023, July 19). *Construction Project Cost Estimation: Best Practices and Tools for Construction Professionals.* MCG Quantity Surveyors - We Do Depreciation Differently; MCG Quantity Surveyors. https://www.mcgqs.com.au/construction-cost/construction-project-cost-estimation-best-practices-and-tools-for-construction-professionals/

Netscher, P. (2017, April 16). *Are you ethical? Unfortunately, many businesses carry out unethical practices. Contractors and the construction industry are often viewed as being unethical.* Linkedin.com. https://www.linkedin.com/pulse/ethics-construction-what-unethical-behaviours-why-should-netscher

Newsmantraa. (2022, July 10). *Construction Robots Market Envisioned to Generate a CAGR of 13.56% from 2022-2031 - Digital Journal.* Digital Journal. https://www.digitaljournal.com/pr/construction-robots-market-envisioned-to-generate-a-cagr-of-13-56-from-2022-2031

On-Screen Takeoff Integrator. (2021). Sage.com. https://help-sageestimating.na.sage.com/en-us/20_1/Content/menus/OSTIntegrator_Interface.htm

peter.cholakis@verizon.net. (2020, December 7). *Collaborative Construction Cost Estimating drive improve productivity.* 4BT. https://4bt.us/collaborative-construction-cost-estimating/

PlanSwift.com. (2015). PlanSwift.com. https://www.planswift.com/

Precise Estimate. (2024). Preciseestimateinc.com. https://www.preciseestimateinc.com/about.html

Project Management for Construction: Cost Estimation. (2024). Cmu.edu. https://www.cmu.edu/cee/projects/PMbook/05_Cost_Estimation.html

Rajan, S. (2023, July 13). *Linarc.* Linarc. https://linarc.com/buildspace/managing-unexpected-costs-in-construction-projects/

RSMeans data. (2023). Rsmeans.com. https://www.rsmeans.com/

Swanek, T. (2021, September 22). *New Report Finds Construction Contractors Struggling to Find Workers, Materials.* Uschamber.com. https://www.uschamber.com/infrastructure/new-report-finds-construction-contractors-struggling-find-workers-materials

Table 9. Producer price indexes for commodity and service groupings and individual items, not seasonally adjusted. (n.d.). https://www.bls.gov/web/ppi/ppitable09.pdf

Takeoff Monkey - About us. (2024, January 16). Takeoff Monkey. https://www.takeoffmonkey.com/about-us/

Takeoff Software for Precise Estimates | Houzz Pro. (2024). Houzz.com. https://www.houzz.com/for-pros/takeoff

The construction estimating process, steps and strategies. (2022, January 20). Buildxact US. https://www.buildxact.com/us/blog/construction-estimating-process/

Top 6 Construction Estimating Certifications for Preconstruction Professionals - NICHE SSP.

(2024). Nichessp.com. https://www.nichessp.com/blog/construction-estimating-certification

Transparency Market Research. (2022, July 7). *Construction Robots Market is predicted to Expand at a CAGR of 15.3% during the Forecast Period, TMR Study.* GlobeNewswire News Room; Transparency Market Research. https://www.globenewswire.com/news-release/2022/07/07/2475861/0/en/Construction-Robots-Market-is-predicted-to-Expand-at-a-CAGR-of-15-3-during-the-Forecast-Period-TMR-Study.html

Trimble MEP. (2024). Trimble.com. https://mep.trimble.com/en/mechanical-solutions/estimating-and-takeoff/trimble-autobid-mechanical

Vallerand, P. (2020, December 4). *Note : This blog post was first published on Strategia Conseil website. How much time did you spend managing conflicts at work this week? A study conducted in the United States reveals that employees spend an average of 2.* Linkedin.com. https://www.linkedin.com/pulse/5-methods-resolving-construction-disputes-patrick

Web. (2024). *Construction plan quantity takeoff service.* Globalintegra.com. https://www.globalintegra.com/lp/construction-plan-quantity-takeoff/?gad_source=1&gclid=CjwKCAiAzJOtBhALEiwAtwj8tiRWJoH7M3p5gwZ7MDFw-Eh1KnOkgOkFhv6r0tb07fwqgLlFYSMg8hoC0ZMQAvD_BwE

What Is BIM | Building Information Modeling | Autodesk. (2023, August 8). Autodesk.com. https://www.autodesk.com/solutions/aec/bim?mktvar002=5841872|SEM|20084287329|159000115144|kwd-294971741747&utm_-source=GGL&utm_medium=SEM&utm_campaign=GGL_AEC_Re-vit_AMER_US_Visits_SEM_NBR_New_EX_0000_5841872_&ut-m_id=5841872&utm_term=kwd-294971741747&gad_-source=1&gclid=Cj0KCQiAnrOtBhDIARIsAFsSe52wbck36dLLncxXo2EQw_w-QVUsILAQfWCqkGrOlpOEuNNc_hQgIZqkaAgxiEALw_wcB

What is RSMeans data? (2023). Rsmeans.com. https://www.rsmeans.com/info/contact/about-us

Why You Must Clarify Construction Scope of Work | Horst Construction. (2022, March 22). Horst Construction. https://www.horstconstruction.com/news-and-blog/why-its-essential-to-clarify-your-construction-projects-scope-of-work/

Wikipedia Contributors. (2023, February 19). *16 Divisions.* Wikipedia; Wikimedia Foundation. https://en.wikipedia.org/wiki/16_Divisions#:~:text=The%2016%20-Divisions%20of%20construction,in%20the%20U.S.%20and%20Canada.

Williams, G. (2015, April 22). *All About Post-War Architecture.* HGTV; HGTV. https://www.hgtv.com/design/decorating/design-101/all-about-post-war-architecture

ABOUT THE AUTHOR

Paul "P.D." Mason lives in the upper Midwest region of the United States with his wife and his trusted writing companion, a knee-high pit bull terrier mix named Sugar. Paul is an independent author writing for SugarDog Publishing and has written multiple fiction and non-fiction books on various topics and fictional storylines that resonate with his readers.

ALSO BY P.D. MASON

Financially Smart Career Planning For Teens: The Roadmap to Making Informed Decisions In An Uncertain Job Market, Prevent Feeling Overwhelmed & Analysis Paralysis To Achieve Affordable College Degrees(2023, SugarDog Publishing)

Apprenticeship Career Planning for Teens: A Comprehensive Guide to Securing Apprenticeships in High Demand Industries Without Taking on Years of College Debt (2023, SugarDog Publishing)

Skilled Trade Career Planning For Teens: The Handbook of Lucrative Skilled Trades & High Paying Occupations That Don't Require Expensive College Degrees (2023, SugarDog Publishing)

Construction Project Management 101: For Beginners & New Graduates (2023, SugarDog Publishing)

Hands-On Career Planning For Teens: Success Without Student Loans (The Complete Three Book Series) (2023, SugarDog Publishing)

Travel Japan: Unveiling Culture, Language & Local Gems (2023, SugarDog Publishing)

8 Simple Techniques For Easy Kitchen Knife Sharpening: Keep Your Home Kitchen Knives Sharp Using Trusted Tools, Methods & Techniques Taught By Professionals! (2023, SugarDog Publishing)

Made in the USA
Monee, IL
16 July 2024